Drama
C000185002

THE BEST YEARS OF YOUR LIFE

CLIVE JERMAIN

AND

LIVES WORTH LIVING

LAWRENCE EVANS · JANE NASH

Introduction and activities by
Shelagh Pritchard

Heinemann Educational,
a division of Heinemann Publishers (Oxford) Ltd
Halley Court, Jordan Hill, Oxford OX2 8EJ

OXFORD LONDON EDINBURGH
MADRID ATHENS BOLOGNA PARIS
MELBOURNE SYDNEY AUCKLAND SINGAPORE TOKYO
IBADAN NAIROBI HARARE GABORONE PORTSMOUTH NH (USA)

The Best Years of Your Life copyright © Clive Jermain 1986
Lives Worth Living copyright © The Belgrade Theatre in Education
Company 1983
Introduction and activities copyright © 1993 Shelagh Pritchard
All rights reserved

First published in the *Heinemann Plays* series 1993
97 96 95 94 93
10 9 8 7 6 5 4 3 2 1

A catalogue record for this book is available from the British Library on request.
ISBN 0 435 23294 0

All rights whatsoever in these plays are fully protected and application for permission to perform them by professional and amateur companies must be addressed to: Noel Gray Artists, 19 Denmark Street, London WC2H 8NA, for *The Best Years of Your Life* and to The Administrator, Belgrade Theatre in Education Company, Belgrade Theatre, Corporation Street, Coventry, CV1 1GS, for *Lives Worth Living*. No performance may take place unless a licence has first been obtained.

Cover design by Keith Pointing

Designed by Jeffery White Creative Associates

Typeset by Taurus Graphics, Kidlington, Oxon

Printed by Clays Ltd, St Ives plc

Acknowledgements
The publishers would like to thank copyright holders for the use of their material. The publishers would be glad to hear from any unacknowledged sources.

CONTENTS

INTRODUCTION

Five hundred million people in the world are disabled[1] – roughly one in ten and yet disability remains an issue largely ignored by people until they are forced to face it. A relative becomes ill or a child with a disability is born into a family, and relationships change in response to internal and external pressures.

Have you ever considered what happens to mentally handicapped people when they leave education, or when their parents are no longer able to care for them? Have you ever thought about how a wheelchair user fills up his car at a self-service station, or how a handicapped parent might attend your school on open evening, or what happens when a family with a wheelchair user wants to go on holiday? Probably not. Why should you?

The Best Years of Your Life and *Lives Worth Living* explore how disability affects family life and how both the disabled and the non-disabled adjust to the situation. The plays have a positive and hopeful message as we see characters responding with dignity and courage.

The Best Years of Your Life

The Best Years of Your Life is about Robert, a young man of seventeen whose promising career as a footballer is ended when he contracts spinal cancer. We learn in the early scenes of the play that his illness cannot be treated and he has only

---

1 UNESCO *Final report on human rights and disability*. July 1991.

months to live. Cancer is always tragic but here we are confronted with a character on the brink of manhood who should have had his whole life ahead of him. Robert's illness is frequently set against the fitness and energy of the football club which seems to emphasise his helplessness, and he is faced with the constant reminders of what he might have been.

The play asks us to consider some of the physical problems that a wheelchair user might face and what 'chemotherapy' involves, as Robert struggles to come to terms with his disability and how others now see him.

But mostly we are privileged to share the emotional traumas that the family, Robert, his brother Mark and his father, deal with; the sadness and despair but also the strength of love that grows between the characters.

The writer, Clive Jermain, had to give up his ambition to become a television cameraman when he was diagnosed as having spinal cancer at the age of seventeen. He then took up writing for TV. His play *The Best Years of Your Life* was broadcast by the BBC in 1986 and Clive then adapted it for stage where it has been performed by many theatre companies and schools since. Clive died at the age of 22 in 1988.

This version of *The Best Years of Your Life* is the version written for the stage.

Lives Worth Living

Lives Worth Living explores what happens to a family when the parent carer dies and the responsibility for looking after mentally handicapped Mark seems to have passed on to his sister. The play asks if this role should automatically become the daughter's and would we expect the same of a man? We are also asked to consider how Mark feels about his future, are his wishes taken into account or is his life simply arranged by others?

The title *Lives Worth Living* applies to both Mark and his sister Julie. They both have the right to freedom, independence and self-determination, but how do they go about taking those rights? We are given an interesting insight into a relationship where brother and sister clearly love each other but that alone is not enough for either of their lives to be fulfilled and meaningful.

We are also asked to consider how society views the mentally handicapped, from people who hurl abuse in the street to those who 'employ' Mark for £4.00 a week.

After the play texts, you will find ideas for follow-up work. The first section, *Keeping Track*, can be followed scene-by-scene as you read the play and contains questions and simple exercises to help you think more clearly and deeply about what is raised in each scene. The second section, *Explorations*, has larger activities and encourages you to think more broadly about the themes and issues raised by each play as a whole. It also contains some exercises which will help if you are putting on a performance of the play.

Shelagh Pritchard

The Best Years of Your Life

(Stage Version)

Clive Jermain

LIST OF CHARACTERS

Steve
Dave Gibb
Robert
Father
Mark
Dr Hammond
Nurse
Mrs Hurst
Reg
Old man
Paula
Linda
Player
1st boy
2nd boy
Neil
Gary
Doctor

THE BEST YEARS OF YOUR LIFE

Scene One

Chelsea F.C. dressing-room, day.

In the background we hear the sound of players being put through their paces, the distant noises of panting and puffing, the odd bit of larking around, accompanied by shouts of encouragement from the coach.

Items of clothing lie strewn across the floor and over a bench.

A young apprentice, dressed in Chelsea kit, stands centre stage working out, touching his toes, stretching his hamstrings, etc.

After a few seconds he leaves as Steve comes on stage, dressed in kit and carrying a pair of football boots.

Steve is a good-looking eighteen-year-old and has a mature, easy-going character.

He sits on the bench and starts to put his boots on as Dave Gibb enters.

Steve Oh, hello.

Dave (*Weakly.*) Oh, hi.

Steve Cor, you look a bit worse for wear. What you been up to?

Dave (*Sitting.*) I went to Jim West's 21st last night at the Anchor.

Steve Oh yeah, course. How d'it go?

Dave Really well – you missed a good night. We got him one of those roly-poly grams. You should have seen her – she was gross! You've never seen so much fat.

Steve (*Smiling.*) Oh, I'd loved to have seen Jim's face.

Dave So would we. Once she stood in front of him none of us could see anything.

As Dave gets into the story he becomes more excited and animated as:

And you should have seen the size of her ... (*Gestures breasts.*) They were huge. Tell you what, Sam Fox looked like she had prunes compared with her.

Steve laughs.

If you'd put her in 'The Sun' she'd fill page three and the whole of the paper.

They both laugh.

So why didn't you come?

Steve Doing my family duty. It was my great gran's birthday so I went with my parents down to Southend to see her – she was 87. I bet that's how old you feel now, eh?

Dave (*Laughs.*) Something like that.

Steve Oh, well, once you get out on to that pitch in that fresh air and start limbering up you'll feel ... terrible!

Dave Cheers.

Steve Don't mention it. You can do the same for me one day.

Dave (*Getting his own back.*) I will.

Steve laughs. There is a silence as the two put on their boots. Then:

Today's the day that Robert goes down for his operation, isn't it?

Steve Yeah. I rang the hospital this morning to try and talk to him. I just wanted to wish him good luck, you know, but they were already getting him ready to go down so I couldn't talk to him. Anyway the nurse said that she'd pass on the message. (*Looks at watch.*)

Pause.

Dave It's funny isn't it, to think of him, there, in hospital and to think that not long ago he was here, with us, playing ...

Steve Mmmm. But he'll be back, you watch. Rob's a fighter. And a bloody good player. He'll be back.

Steve then jumps up and stamps both feet on the ground, getting used to his boots. Then:

Right, see you out there ...

Dave Yeah ...

Steve dashes off stage leaving Dave looking very thoughtful.

Scene Two

Waiting area, hospital, day.

Two men sit waiting, both look tired and bored. The first, a good-looking man in his very early twenties, dressed casually in jeans, jacket, sits still, almost contentedly. The second, a slightly rough-looking, ungroomed man in his mid-forties, who sits uneasily, fidgeting all the time. The young man is Robert's brother, the elder is his father. We join them in their wait. The father continues to fidget, uneasily. He then leans forward and picks up an old magazine from a coffee table, which he flicks through, with no interest. He throws the magazine down, then sits back.

After a pause ...

Father I'm going to get a drink or something. Do you want anything?

Mark No.

Father Do you want something to eat, a sandwich?

Mark No. No, I couldn't eat anything.

A pause. Then the father starts to rise as Dr Hammond approaches.

Dr Hammond Sorry to keep you waiting, Mr Clark. Would you like to come this way …

The father hesitates for a second then follows the doctor to his desk.

Do sit down.

Slowly the father sits. The doctor then sits, puts on a pair of spectacles, opens a file in front of him and studies it for a few seconds. Then closing the file …

Mr Clark, I'm afraid what I have to tell you isn't going to be very easy. As you know, in the past we have tried treating your son's cancer with various courses of chemotherapy and radiotherapy, which for some time slowed down the rapid growth of, what I warned you, was a highly malignant spinal tumour. Now Robert's tumour was made particularly difficult to treat, because of its location in the spinal cord. Not only is the spinal cord very delicate but to try and operate on any area of the spinal cord is not only very tricky, but dangerous, which is why we put off the question of surgery for as long as we could. Am I making myself clear so far?

The father nods.

However, after the sudden onset of paralysis which Robert suffered a few weeks ago we decided that the best plan was to operate and take a look at what was going on. (*Pause.*) I'm afraid that what we found was slightly worse than we had anticipated. There was a large increase in the growth of the tumour, which had spread further down the spinal cord.

The father sits in stunned silence.

Father So, when will he be out of that chair then, walking again?

Dr Hammond I don't think that he will. As I've tried to explain …

Father You mean he … You mean he's gonna be a cripple for the rest of his life?

Dr Hammond Well I wouldn't have put it quite like that, but for the life that he has left to him, yes. As I've tried to explain, we feel now that we have done everything we possibly can. I have to be honest with you. Robert hasn't a great deal of time left. (*Pause.*) Now at the moment Robert knows nothing … I have to ask you whether you think he should be told or not. He seems to me to be a very intelligent boy, a sensible lad …

Father (*Getting up, angrily.*) Then you'd better tell him then, hadn't ya?

Dr Hammond You want me to tell him.

Father Yes. After all, you're the one who buggered up the operation, aren't you?

Dr Hammond (*Rising.*) Mr Clark …

The father ignores him and walks on. The doctor sighs and sits, as the father walks off, dazed …

(*Eagerly rising.*) What'd he say, Dad? 'Ow did the operation go? (*Pause.*) Dad?

The father ignores him. Mark catches hold of him, as …

Mark Dad, what'd he say, ow'd it go, the operation, ow'd it go?

Father (*After a pause.*) They couldn't remove it all. It had spread further down. Too big, he said.

Mark What does that mean?

Father It means they can't do anything more.

Mark When will he be out of the chair?

Father He won't. They can't do no more. He'll never walk again and he probably won't be 'ere long either … I'm gonna get a drink.

He goes to move on. Mark catches hold of him, again, as …

Mark What'd you mean? What'd you mean?

Father I don't know, I don't know. It's all over. They can't do no more … Look I've gotta get a drink.

He pushes Mark off and walks out of view leaving Mark visibly shocked and anxious.

Scene Three

Hospital ward, day.

Robert is sitting up in bed. A young student nurse is standing by his side affixing a hard collar to him.

Nurse (*Stepping back.*) How's that feel?

Robert (*Pulling a face.*) Uncomfortable.

Nurse You'll get used to it.

Robert (*Pause.*) Can I 'ave me mirror a minute?

The nurse then passes him a small mirror as she starts to pack Robert's wash things into a wash-bag.

(*Robert looks into mirror.*) Oh God it looks terrible, I'll never be able to go out in it.

Nurse (*Taking mirror.*) Of course you will.

She places the mirror back into the wash-bag and zips it up, as …

Anyway, it won't be for long.

Robert How long?

Nurse I don't know, that's something you'll have to ask the doctors.

The nurse then places the wash-bag to one side and starts to tidy the bed. After a few seconds Dr Hammond enters and makes his way over to the bottom of Robert's bed.

Robert (*Looking up, surprised.*) Oh, Morning, Dr Hammond.

Dr Hammond Good morning, Robert.

The nurse discreetly exits.

How are you feeling today?

Robert Oh, not too bad. (*Indicating collar.*) Apart from this thing.

Dr Hammond You shouldn't have to wear that for too long. Just till we make sure that everything inside has healed up, er, properly.

Robert Oh, I still can't move my legs yet. And my arms still feel very weak. I asked Dr Simmonds, this morning, when things would start getting better, but he said to ask you.

Dr Hammond sighs. He then moves to the edge of the bed and sits down. After a short pause …

Dr Hammond Robert, what I'm about to tell you I wouldn't be able to tell all seventeen-year-olds but I know that you're a very intelligent and sensible chap. Unfortunately, your operation wasn't as successful as we'd hoped it would be. Now we carried out an extensive operation on your spinal cord but I'm afraid what we found was rather worse than we had anticipated and we felt that the risks and dangers involved in operating further were just too great. So I'm afraid that we were only able to remove part of it.

Robert stunned, swallows hard. After a pause …

And to answer your question, when will things start getting better, and your movements come back. I don't think that things will, and I think the likelihood is they may even get worse, as your cancer progresses.

Robert is totally shattered. Pause.

Anyway, I've spoken to your father and we both think that it would be a good idea for you to go home, get out of hospital, we'll give you something to take home for the pain and we'll make an appointment for you to come back in about three weeks' time. (*Places his hand on Robert's.*) We all tried our very best for you, I'm terribly sorry. Anyway I'm sure you've got a lot to think about.

Dr Hammond rises and leaves.

Robert stares straight ahead, completely devastated, tears form in his eyes but he struggles to hold them back.

After a long pause the nurse rushes in and busily tidies Robert's bed.

Nurse You've got a visitor, Robert. It's your brother. Shall I let him in?

She receives no answer. She then walks out. We hear her talking out of view and after a few seconds Mark slowly enters and makes his way over to Robert. Mark is entirely at a loss for what to say next. He grasps at something.

Mark Nice that nurse, hey? Tasty.

No response from Robert.

Dad'll be along soon, 'e's just parking the car. Somebody told him to go round the back, there's a ramp round there — it'll be easier for the chair and that.

Mark takes another desperate grab at an opening gambit.

'Ow you feelin' then?

Robert just looks up at Mark and stares at him coldly. After a long pause ...

Robert (*Holding back the emotion.*) D-D-D-D-D'you know?

Mark is rather taken aback by the question. He takes a deep breath, closes his eyes, and nods.

Robert bursts into tears, covering his eyes with his hands.

Oh God no. No. I'm gonna be a cripple. I'm gonna be a cripple and die. Aren't I, Mark?

Mark No. I mean ... come on, don't think about it.

Robert Why? God, why me?

Robert continues to cry. Mark watches helpless, trying to hold back his own tears.

Scene Four

Robert and Mark's bedroom, interior, day.

A set of bunk beds and several pieces of Chelsea memorabilia. Mark is having difficulty in trying to negotiate Robert in his wheelchair through the door to the bedroom.

Mark Won't get through ...

Robert Yes it will, if you just straighten it up.

Mark Have to ask Dad to get the doors widened ...

Robert No, it's all right, just — straighten it up here and push it straight through ...

Mark manages.

Mark There we go.

Mark pushes Robert into the room then retrieves a suitcase from just outside as Robert looks thoughtfully round the room smiling. Mark places the suitcase on the bed as ...

Afraid it's still as untidy as ever.

Robert No. It's great. It's funny, I'd almost forgotten what it looked like, it's great to be back.

Mark smiles.

Mark Oh yeah, got something for you. It came a couple of days ago, but I didn't wanna fetch it into the hospital in case it got, oh, lost or screwed up.

He takes out a brown envelope from under his pillow and holds it out to Robert.

Robert What is it?

Mark Well open it and see.

Robert cautiously takes it. He starts to open it with some difficulty.

(*Mark takes the envelope.*) Here, let's give you a hand.

He takes out a photograph and passes it to Robert.

Robert's reaction is mixed. He is pleased but curious.

Robert It's Bryan Robson.

Mark Yeah. See what it says. 'To Robert, Get well soon, Bryan Robson'.

Robert How did you get him to sign it?

Mark I just wrote to him at United, told him you were one of this country's up and coming footballers and that you were in 'ospital and could he send you a signed photo to cheer you up.

Robert What d'you say?

Mark Eh?

Robert What did you tell him?

Mark Can't remember. I just said, you were in 'ospital, you were ill, you know with –

Robert What? With what?

Mark Well, you know, with –

Robert Cancer. You can say it without catching it, you know. Cancer. I know what I've got. You spell it C A N C E R.

Mark (*Embarrassed.*) Yeah, I know.

A pause.

(*Taking the photo.*) I'll put it up next to yours, OK?

Mark places the photograph on the wall next to one of Robert. After a silence as Mark places the photograph on the wall he turns.

Now you're 'ome, me an' you could do lots of things, go lots of places. We break up in a couple of weeks and Colin said if there's anywhere we wanna go he'll take us as long as we give him a couple of days' warning. He's only got an old Imp but it'd get us there and back, and he's quite a good driver, we've only had the odd hair-raising moment. So, where would you like to go?

Robert (*Thinking.*) I don't know.

Mark Oh well, there's no rush. You got a couple of weeks to think about it, then, when you've thought where you wanna go we'll fix something up, eh?

Robert nods and smiles.

Father enters carrying another suitcase. He places it on the bed. He looks at Robert and Mark. They look at him.

Father I'll just put the kettle on.

Mark It won't suit you, Dad.

Father Eh?

Mark Won't be able to get your head through the spout.

Robert and Mark smile. The father, not understanding, leaves. Robert and Mark laugh.

'Spose I'd better give him a hand. What d'you want – tea or coffee?

Robert Oh, tea please.

Mark Right.

Mark leaves. After a pause Robert turns and looks around the room again. After a few seconds we hear two voices in the background. One belongs to Mark. Both are audible, but unintelligible. After a few seconds Robert turns as David Gibb enters. He stands tentatively, feeling very uneasy, seeing Robert for the first time.

Robert (*Surprised.*) Hello Dave.

Dave Hi. Mark said that you were coming home today, so I thought I'd pop round and see how you are. (*Pause.*) Some of the lads and me, well, we were gonna come and visit you in 'ospital, but, well, what with training and things we just didn't get round to it. John's just started us on this new training programme. It's really knackering. You're lucky you've missed it.

Robert (*Despondently.*) Yeah.

Dave Back at the club we 'ad sort of a whip round. We couldn't think what to get you so we got you these.

He holds out two packages. Robert hesitates.

Robert Thanks.

Robert clumsily takes the package.

Dave You all right?

Robert Yeah, yeah, fine.

Robert starts to open the package.

Dave I went out and chose that one myself, I knew you didn't have it and it's a really good book.

Robert takes out the book and starts to browse through.

There's some really good photos in it as well. There's a great one of Dave Webb scoring the goal that got us the FA Cup. (*After a second, pointing.*) There it is.

Robert Oh yeah. 1970. Glory, glory days, eh? (*He flicks through to the end.*) You're right, it's a good book. Cheers.

Robert looks at the other package.

What's this?

Dave Oh, we thought that might cheer you up.

Robert opens the package to reveal several dirty magazines.

Robert Oh, I see.

He flicks through a few pages then stops at one in particular. He holds the magazine up and rotates it through 360°, to view it from all angles.

Wow, what a way to go, eh?

Dave If you like, some of the lads and me could come round one night.

Robert No, no. Tell you what, why don't we leave it a couple of days, give me time to settle back, down, an' I'll give you a ring and we'll arrange a real night out, a real night on the town, eh?

Dave OK, then. (*Pause.*) Well, I'll let you get on then.

Robert Yeah.

Dave Right.

Dave goes to leave.

Robert Dave.

Dave Yeah.

Robert (*Pause.*) Would you thank the lads for me?

Dave Yeah, course. (*Pause.*) Anyway, I'd better be off. We've got training later.

Robert Thanks for coming.

Dave Yeah. See you around.

Robert closes his eyes and gives a loud sigh. After a few seconds Mark enters.

Mark (*Glancing around.*) Oh, Dave gone? I came to see if he wanted a coffee.

Robert He had to rush off. He's got training later.

Mark Oh. Nice of him to come round though, wasn't it?

Robert Mmm.

Mark (*Spotting magazines.*) Ah, what's that?

Robert Oh, some of the lads had a bit of a whip round. Thought they might cheer me up.

Mark (*Browsing through.*) They certainly bring a smile to your face. We can have a good look at them later. Think I'd better hide 'em for now, in case Dad sees 'em. I'll hide 'em under my pillow, all right?

Robert Yeah.

Mark (*Placing magazines under his pillow.*) Then, if I wake up in the middle of the night with a sudden passionate urge I'll have something to turn to.

Robert What happens if I wake up with a passionate urge?

Mark (*Thinks.*) Well just give us a shout and I'll pass them down to ya.

They both laugh.

(*Spotting book.*) This from them as well?

Robert Yeah. (*Hands Mark book.*) It's a really good book actually, Dave went out and chose it.

Mark (*Browsing through.*) Mmm. (*He spots an amusing*

photo and laughs.) Look at that kit, eh? And those shorts. (*He holds out the book for Robert to see. They both laugh.*) They're nearly down to his ankles …

From off-stage we hear:

Father Are you making this tea?

Mark looks up and tuts.

Mark If 'e had brains 'e'd be dangerous … I'd better give him a hand.

Mark hands the book back to Robert and exits. Robert gazes around the room again then looks down at the book on his lap.

Scene Five

Kitchen, interior, morning.

Robert, Father and Mark are sitting round the kitchen table upon which are the remains of breakfast. The father is sitting reading a newspaper. Mark is sitting staring at a textbook and Robert is looking down at a bowl of cereal.

Father (*Folding up newspaper.*) Oh well better get going. (*Rising.*) See you both later then.

Mark See ya, Dad.

Robert Yeah, bye.

The father goes. After a pause …

Mark He suggested we go down the pub tonight since you're back home and it's Friday. Who knows, might get a free pint out of 'im.

Robert (*Smiles.*) No chance.

Mark What's up. Not 'ungry?

Robert No. Time I took my pills anyway.

Mark D'you wanna hand?

Robert Yeah all right.

There is a tray of assorted tablets on the table.

Mark Is this all of them?

Robert Yeah.

Mark slides the tray towards him.

Mark One of each is it?

Robert No. What's that one you got there?

Mark (*Squints at the label.*) Dia – something.

Robert Diamorphine. Four of them.

Mark Four.

Robert Yeah.

Mark pours out four pills.

Put them in that cup there.

Mark puts them into a small plastic cup.

Now look for Maxalon.

Mark does so.

Mark There we go.

Robert One of them.

Mark One right ...

He takes out one pill.

Robert Put it in the cup.

Mark does so.

Now Dexamethazone, two.

Mark (*Looking.*) Dexa ... Dexa ... here we are. Two?

Robert Yeah.

Mark puts two pills in the cup.

One Baclofen.

Mark puts another pill in the cup.

Two Dorbanex and that's it.

Mark puts two more pills in the cup, then:

Mark There we go. Cor, d'you have to take all that lot?

Robert Yeah. 'Ave to take that lot three times a day.

Mark Cor. What do they all do?

Robert Do? I dunno. Yes I do. The Diamorphine takes away the pain but it makes you feel sick, so the Maxalon takes away the sickness. Dexamethazone's a steroid, like athletes take, it builds you up.

Mark Mr Anabolic Steroid of London, eh?

Robert (*A smile.*) The Baclofen stops you twitching and jumping all over the place. (*Robert starts to twitch and wobble in order to demonstrate, exaggeratedly.*) And the Dorbanex makes you crap, because all the other pills bung you up.

Mark Bloody hell.

Robert reaches for the cup.

Wanna glass of water to help 'em down with?

Robert No, what you gotta do now is put them in a cocktail shaker, shaken not stirred, for a few minutes, then add ice and lemon.

Mark But we ain't got a cocktail shaker.

Robert (*Smiling.*) You wally, ordinary milk will do.

Mark pours Robert out a glass of milk. Robert tips the pills into his mouth and with one swig of milk takes them in one.

Mark (*Glancing at his watch.*) Shit is that the time? Better get going or I'll miss the bus. Colin said he'll drop us back, so I should be home a bit earlier. Will you be all right?

Robert Yeah.

Mark takes a final mouthful of tea.

Mark Don't worry about any of the washing-up. Mrs Hurst'll do it when she comes round later.

Robert Oh not Mrs Hurst –

Mark I told you last night, Dad asked her if she'd pop in and see that you're all right and she said she'd cook you a bit of lunch as well. She's not that bad. At least you won't be on your own all day.

Mark gets up and starts to pack his book and other bits into a sports bag.

How are you feeling now?

Robert OK.

Mark You sure?

Robert (*Sharply.*) Yes I'm OK Mark! OK?

A slight pause.

Mark Listen if you need anything I've written the numbers and left them there (*pointing*) by the phone – there's Dad's number at work, and my number at college. And you know Mrs Hurst's number don't you?

Robert Yes. Stop fussing.

Mark Sorry. It's only because I worry.

Robert There's no need. I'll be all right.

Mark OK then but you will promise to ring if there's anything won't you?

Robert Yes.

Mark OK then. See you later.

Robert Bye.

Mark hovers a moment longer, then goes.

Mark Bye then.

Robert Yeah bye.

After a few seconds we hear the front door slam.

Robert sighs with relief, alone for the first time in the flat. Total silence. Robert moves in closer to the table and starts to tidy up. As he is moving the bowls together he knocks the milk over but just about saves it. He gives a loud sigh. He then moves round the table and picks up the newspaper which his father was reading. He flicks through it uninterestedly to the end then places the paper back down. He then stops and thinks to himself for a few seconds. After a pause he moves closer to the telephone. Thinking to himself, he tries to remember a number. The telephone is an old dial model. He puts his finger into one of the holes and starts to dial. He completes one dial then starts on the next. His finger slips out and the dial spins back to the beginning. He tuts to himself and starts again. Slowly and concentrating hard he dials two more numbers. On the third his finger again slips out and the dial spins back to the beginning. He slams the receiver back down and:

Damn.

After a pause he tries again. Slowly and with great care he starts to dial. He manages four numbers and then on the fifth he again loses his hold and the dial spins back to the beginning. Full of anger and frustration he throws the receiver and …

Shit.

He then bursts into tears. After a few seconds the doorbell chimes. Robert hears it, looks up, dries his eyes with his cuffs, but doesn't move. It chimes again. He still doesn't move. From off-stage we hear:

Mrs Hurst Robert?

The doorbell chimes again.

Robert? Are you all right? Can you get to the door, love? I haven't got a key, you see. Robert?

There is a few seconds silence. Robert relaxes. He is then startled by a knocking which appears to come from behind him. He moves over to another part of the stage as from off-stage we hear again:

Robert, what are you doing? I can see you, let me in. Don't just sit there, love.

But Robert does. After a pause.

Are you all right? Robert, let me in love. I've got you your lunch, I've made you a nice quiche. I know you like quiche.

Robert (*Whispers.*) I hate quiche. Just leave me alone.

Scene Six

Pub, interior, night.

Friday night and the pub is packed, full of noisy music, etc. Robert is alone momentarily at a corner table. After a few seconds Mark reaches the table carrying two pints of beer. He places them down on the table.

Mark (*Sitting.*) There we go. What's all this Dad's just told me about not letting Mrs Hurst in?

Robert I did let her in.

Mark Yeah, but not until she'd rung Dad and 'e was on his way home. 'E's not too happy about it, Rob.

Robert He'll get over it.

Mark Yeah, but why Rob?

Robert (*Snapping.*) Thought this was supposed to be a night out, not the big inquisition, right?

Mark Yeah all right, all right. (*Looks over at his father standing at the bar, drinking and chatting.*) Look at him jawing away. Talks to his mates, never talks to us though. Funny that, isn't it?

A man approaches, laden with empties, middle-aged. A known character in the pub, called Reg.

Reg Hallo hallo. If it ain't my old mate Rob. Nice to see you out. Welcome back to the land of the living then mate. (*Pause.*) 'Ow long before you're up and out of that chair and 'elpin' us prop up the bar then, eh, Rob?

Robert (*Quietly.*) Soon.

Reg Been talking to your father. 'Ow long you been in that 'ospital for? Six weeks was it?

Robert Yeah.

Mark rises and hovers as:

Reg You wanna be careful in hospitals. You know why? Mate of mine went in, had a bit of gangrene in his leg, so they had to take it off, see, only trouble is, they took off the wrong leg. No really. He woke up from the operation, they'd taken the wrong one off, said they were sorry and all that, but they'd have to take the other one off, the one they was supposed to have taken off in the first place. They asked him how he felt about that. Well he – (*splutters*) well he didn't have a leg to stand on really did he? (*He guffaws at his joke.*) Get it? Didn't have a leg to stand on. (*There is no reaction.*) Didn't have a leg to stand on. It's a joke, it's not true –

Mark Very funny, Reg. (*To Robert.*) D'you wanna packet of crisps?

Robert No.

Mark walks off towards bar.

Reg Oi son, sense of humour? Lost our sense of humour have we? (*Turning to Robert.*) Used to be a bit of a laugh, your brother, bit of a joker, liked jokes.

Robert Yeah. Just not in the mood for 'em.

Reg Say no more, say no more. A subtle hint is as good as anything to me. Leave you to it. Nice to see you back though. (*He catches sight of someone else in the pub, calls to them and then rushes off.*)

There are a few seconds silence. Robert waits patiently. He then becomes aware of an old man, sitting nearby, staring at him. He turns a bit further to see, then turns away as:

Old man 'Ello sonny. What's happened to you then? Had an accident, have you?

Robert ignores him.

My cousin broke his neck, playing rugby. Crippled him for life, it did.

(*Pause.*) *Robert keeps looking away.*

(*Continuing.*)

Nice chair you've got there. Ought to try and get one of those speedy electric ones. Can whizz all over the place then.

Robert (*Anxious.*) Mark.

He then turns towards the bar where he sees Mark talking to someone. As he looks, he spots two girls at the bar. Robert turns quickly back as:

(*Grimacing.*) Oh no.

He freezes for a few seconds, hoping the girls have not seen him but it is too late. The two girls make their way over to him. Paula is a lively young cockney girl. The other girl, Linda, is a very pretty, but quiet girl.

Paula Robert? (*Pause.*) Robert Clark?

Reluctantly he turns and looks at them.

Robert (*Still trying to keep up the pretence.*) Sorry, you talking to me?

Paula Who d'you think we was talking to? You're Robert Clark ain't you?

Robert No.

Paula Yes you is. Remember us? I'm Paula, remember? This is Linda, remember Linda?

Robert No, sorry. You've got the wrong bloke.

Paula No we 'aven't. (*Moving closer.*) Listen, what happened? Linda asked after you down the club the other day, didn't you Lind. They said you were in 'ospital. Did ya 'ave some kinda accident?

Robert Club. What club?

Paula (*Giggling.*) Down the Bridge.

Robert What bridge?

Paula Well it ain't bloody Tower Bridge, is it? Stamford bloody Bridge.

Robert So sorry. Don't know what you're talking about.

Paula then sits and continues, rather enjoying it.

Paula OK, so if you ain't Robert Clark who are you? What's your name?

Robert Harry.

Paula Oh yeah? Harry what?

Robert Um . . . Martini.

Paula Harry Martini, eh?

Robert That's right.

Paula Italian are you, Harry?

Robert That's right.

Paula Don't sound foreign to me, doesn't sound foreign to me. Does he sound foreign to you, Lind? Say something in Italian then.

Robert What?

Paula Say something, in Italian.

Robert (*Thinks.*) Ravioli.

This sets Paula off into fits of giggles. Robert looks helplessly in the direction of Mark, who's still at the bar, chatting.

Paula Martini, eh? (*She sings.*) Any time any place anywhere ... (*Looks at Linda.*) Eh Lind?

Linda just smiles.

There's a wonderful world you can share ... So listen, how long have you got to be stuck in that thing? When will you be up again, playing again?

Robert Playing what?

Paula (*Tuts.*) Football wally.

Robert Dunno what you're talking about, sorry.

Paula Ain't you the wonderboy of the Chelsea youth team then?

Robert No, sorry. Never played football in my life. Can't stand it.

Paula has another fit of laughter. Mark begins to make his way back.

Paula You're a funny one ain't you Rob? He's a funny one ain't he Lind?

Robert You got the wrong bloke. My name's Harry, Harry Martini.

Mark arrives back, tucking into a bag of crisps.

Robert Hello Paula. Haven't seen you around lately. (*To Linda.*) Linda, isn't it?

Linda nods.

Mark (*Offering packet.*) Like a crisp?

Linda nods.

(*Offers to Paula.*) Paula?

Paula No thanks, Mark Martini.

Mark Eh?

Paula Mark Martini isn't it?

Mark still looks blankly at her.

Your brother here's changed his name. To Martini.

Robert is now under tremendous pressure.

Robert (*Wanting to go.*) Mark –

Mark does not notice, instead:

Mark (*To Linda.*) You've grown, Linda. Coming out in all the right places, know what I mean?

Paula Oi, watch it.

Mark Who are you, her mum or something?

Robert Please, Mark –

Mark What's up?

Robert Can we go now?

Mark (*Laughing.*) Steady on, Rob, we've only just arrived, ain't we?

Paula What you calling him Rob for? His name's Harry –

Mark Eh?

Paula Dunno what happened to him in that accident, seems to have lost his memory and all, says he hates football.

Mark Yeah?

Robert (*Anxiously.*) Mark –

Mark Buy you a drink girls? What you having?

Robert is now under unbearable pressure, and just wants to go.

Robert (*Loudly.*) Mark!

The pub falls silent for a second. Robert looks down in embarrassment. After a pause:

Please, Mark, this was a mistake – take me home please –

Mark Yeah OK. Come on then – see you then girls. Maybe we can have a drink another time?

The girls nod.

Mark starts to push Robert out.

Paula Bye Harry. Keep taking the English lessons.

Mark and Robert exit. Paula and Linda watch as they go. Then they both sit.

Linda I reckon it's something a bit serious.

Yeah.

Paula He looked ill. Shame. (*Pause.*) D'you still fancy him though?

Linda Yeah.

Scene Seven

Robert and Mark's bedroom, interior, night.

Robert and Mark are in bed. Mark is in the top bunk – Robert in the lower bunk. The street lamps, together with the final few specks of light, illuminate the room. Robert is sitting up in bed thoughtfully. After a few seconds.

Robert (*Quietly.*) Mark. Are you awake?

Mark groans.

Why d'you leave me tonight?

Mark Leave you, where?

Robert In the pub. You left me there, sitting there.

Mark Only went to get some crisps.

Robert But I saw you over there, chatting.

Mark Well, I bumped into Derek –

Robert And I was stuck there, with Paula, and Linda. I was trapped, couldn't move. I had to rely on you to get me out of there.

Mark (*Still waking up.*) It wasn't for long.

Robert That's why I didn't let Mrs Hurst in today. I wanted to be by myself, have a day on my own. After all it was my first day back home I wanted to see if I could manage, be independent like I used to be. I'm not used to relying, relying on anyone. On Mrs Hurst, on Dad or you. We've both looked after ourselves, brought ourselves up, didn't we – Mark?

Mark Yeah, I know.

A pause.

Robert Used to fancy that Linda. Still do. Think she fancied me too. Used to come down to the ground, watch me play. Think it was me she was watching. Never got round to asking her out though. Well there's a chance gone, eh? Last time I saw her though, and Paula, I was all right. At least I looked all right anyway. And tonight, I had to sit there, trapped, in that thing. At least when I was walking about and I had cancer I was the only one that knew. Now, now everyone knows, knows there's something wrong anyway, and if they don't, they ask. Like that old bloke. D'you know what? He made me feel like some animal, some animal in the zoo, that people go and look and gawp and stare at for as long as they want, then when they've had enough they just walk on. I felt like I was invisible. Everyone just looked at the chair, it was as if I wasn't there. Even Dave didn't recognise me the other day when he came round. To him I wasn't the same person no more.

Mark You've still got your brain.

Robert And what good's that, eh? I'm not going to score goals with it am I? Or play for Chelsea. (*Pause.*) At the club the other lads used to look up to me. I was (*painfully*). hard. Now? Now, I don't even feel human.

Mark They were only trying to be friendly.

Robert Oh yeah. What about Reg?

Mark Yeah. Tasteful little joke, eh?

Robert 'Welcome back to the land of the living.' The land of the living?

Mark You're not going to start taking what Reg says seriously are you? Number one bore of the Dog and Trumpet? Anyway, he doesn't know does he? No one knows. Even now they don't know, do they – I mean, if you don't tell them, how can you expect them to –

Robert (*Defensively.*) Want me to tell them, is that what you want?

A slight pause.

Mark (*Awkwardly.*) I dunno Rob.

Robert (*Bitterly.*) You want me to tell them everything, do ya? Not that I'm just never gonna play football again, but that I'm dying as well. That I probably won't even make it to be eighteen. You could wake up tomorrow morning. Find me dead –

Mark (*Closing eyes.*) Yeah all right.

Robert You ready for that, Mark? Thought about it, have you? What you're gonna do when it happens? Only person who's talked about it so far is the doctor. He faced up to it. Made me face up to it.

A pause.

I'm dying. Don't know what'll happen to me when I do. Where I'll go. I'm frightened. I am. Old people get used to it, so they say. But I'm seventeen, I'm seventeen. So I'm frightened.

Mark (*Suddenly exploding.*) Just shut it, Rob, all right? Shut up!

Mark turns over.

Scene Eight

Sitting-room, interior, night.

Father, now dressed casually, is sitting in an armchair reading the paper. Mark enters. He looks over to his father. There is no reaction. He moves over to the sofa and sits, pensive. He looks at his father several times, there is still no response. After a few seconds:

Mark Dad? (*No response.*) Dad.

Father (*Still behind his paper.*) Mm?

Mark I think – I think it's about time me and you had a talk.

Father (*Still behind his paper.*) What about?

Mark (*Rising.*) What about? What d'you think?

Mark then tears the paper away from his father.

Father 'ere!

Mark (*Whispering harshly.*) D'you really care about him, eh?

Father 'Course I care, what you talking about?

Slight pause. Then the father gets up and moves upstage as:

Mark Dad!

Mark stops Father as:

Robert's been home nearly a week and you've hardly said a word to him.

Father What am I supposed to say?

Mark He's coping with a whole new way of life! He needs help, bit of support, people around, people talking to him. What do you do?

Father He hasn't said anything to me.

Mark Well 'e wouldn't have, would he? You never have been very easy to talk to. Anyway he hasn't got to say anything, surely you can tell by the way he looks at you. I can. I can, because it's the same way I used to look at you when I was little. Every night after school, me and Robert used to come in, get on with our homework and wait for you to come home and do our tea. You'd come in, get our tea, do the washing-up, tidy round, have a bath, then sit and watch TV or go down the pub. D'you know, at times I felt invisible. Used to deliberately stand in your way, hoping you'd talk to me, not just about the sort of day I'd had at school, or what the weather was like, but really talk. But you never did. Anyway, I'm older now, I don't need you to talk to any more, but Robert still does. That's why I just can't understand how you just come home night after night and sit casually back while your son's in the next room and you don't even know if he's going to make it through to next week. I'm sure he could drop dead in front of you and you wouldn't even notice!

Father Oi!

Mark He talked to me about it the other night, about dying. He's frightened. Frightened of it.

Father (*Furiously.*) Don't you dare! Don't you dare talk to me about dying as if you were some kind of expert!

Mark Dad I'm only saying that –

Father (*Not listening.*) I was coping with death while you were still some snotty little kid in short trousers. How old were you when your mother was killed? Five? Six? I'd been married to her for twelve years, twelve years. When your mother died you lost someone who had brought you up and looked after you for six years. Me? I lost everything. I lost the only woman I'd ever loved. Someone that I'd spent ten years of my life with. (*Pause.*) For months afterwards nothing seemed real. I walked round in a daze. It was like having the shit kicked out of ya. I felt empty. Even now, there's still a bit missing. And nobody stopped to give a toss about what I was going through. Everyone was more concerned about how you boys were taking it, about what was going to happen to you. So don't you lecture me about death.

Mark Dad, I didn't realise. You've never talked like this before. But with Mum, she died instantly. You couldn't do anything for her. There was nothing you could do. I know you can't stop Robert dying, but what you can do is give him a bit of time.

The father grabs his coat.

Where you going?

Father (*Putting his coat on.*) For a bit of peace and quiet. Down the pub.

He makes his way off-stage.

Mark (*Bawls.*) O yeah, have another drink! That'll solve everything!

The father is gone. We hear the front door slam shut. Mark sighs then sits on the sofa, defeated.

Scene Nine

Robert and Mark's bedroom, interior, morning.

Robert is tucked up in bed asleep. Mark, in shorts and T-shirt, is on the floor doing press-ups. Mark continues counting as:

Robert (*Waking.*) What's this?

Mark (*Puffing.*) Oh good morning.

Robert Morning.

Mark Keep-fit. Twenty-eight ... twenty-nine ... started doing a bit of keep-fit at weekends ... thirty. (*He collapses on the floor.*) I've already been out for a run this morning, twice round the estate.

Robert Thought you only did that when you had girl problems.

Mark Funny. Tell you what though, certainly loosens you up and makes you feel a bit better after sitting behind a desk all week. (*Pause.*) Oh I forgot to tell you I saw Sue on my way to college the other day.

Robert (*Interested.*) Yeah?

Mark Yeah. She asked after you, you know. Said she'd try and pop in sometime.

Robert (*Shyly.*) Oh. (*A pause.*) I tried to ring her the other day. First day I was back. Couldn't manage it though. Couldn't manage the dial on the phone.

Mark Why didn't you tell me? I'd 'ave dialled the number for you, then left you alone for a quiet, intimate chat.

Robert No. It's all right.

Mark gets up.

Mark Anyway come on. Time you got up. We're going down the Bridge, reserve game, playing Arsenal.

Robert Oh. No thanks. I'd rather not.

Mark But I've already told them you was coming, Rob.

Robert No thanks.

Mark is suddenly angry.

Mark Christ, Rob, what you going to do, spend the rest of your life stuck in here, not seeing anyone, not letting anyone see you? Is that what you want?

Robert Yeah, maybe it is.

Mark Just gonna sit there in that thing all day are yer, feeling sorry for yourself?

Robert Yeah.

Mark You're pathetic you are!

Robert Yeah. I am. Only just noticed, have you? I'm pathetic. Look at me.

Mark They're your mates! They wanna see you!

Robert Yeah well I don't want to see them, all right?

Mark Gonna turn your back on them all, are you, your mates? You've played football with them for three years.

Robert Not gonna play any more though am I? What's the

point of seeing them?

Mark They wanna see you, Rob!

Robert Do they?

Mark Yeah they do.

Robert (*Angrily.*) And where they gonna put me to watch the game, eh? Where am I gonna sit, in cripple corner, wrapped up in a blanket, sitting there with all the raspberry ripples, spastics, dribbling all over the place, waving their rattles? No thanks.

Mark (*Exploding.*) Oh well, sod it, Rob! Suit yourself. You've always been a stubborn little shit! I s'pose you think it's been easy, do you – whole year I've had to deal with it – whole sodding year – answering their sodding questions – why you've had to keep going into hospitals – 'How is he? How's Rob? All right is he? What's the matter with him? When's he coming out?' Think it's easy do you, making up all the lies, telling them you're OK, it's nothing serious, you're on the mend? You try doing it, you sodding do it from now on. Better still, why don't you just go and tell them the truth? It'll be a load off my mind, I can tell you. I'm giving up Rob, that's it, I've finished! It's like living in a sodding morgue here, anyway. I'm off. I've got my own life to live.

Mark moves away as:

Robert (*Quietly.*) Well go and live it then Mark.

Mark What?

Robert I said go and live it then. No one's forcing you to stay.

Mark All right then, I will.

Mark leaves. There is a long pause.

Robert (*Calling out.*) Mark. Mark.

After a few seconds Mark walks slowly back over to Robert.

Mark What?

Robert Where you going?

Mark I told ya, down the Bridge.

Robert Hang on a minute I'm coming with you.

Mark What?

Robert I said I'm coming with you.

Mark But I thought –

Robert Never mind about all that. I've changed my mind! I'm coming with you, all right?

Mark All right. (*Mark then moves the wheelchair in closer to the bed. He then helps Robert to sit up on the edge of the bed. After a second.*) All right?

Robert Yeah.

Mark then helps Robert into the wheelchair.

Scene Ten

Chelsea F.C. changing-room, interior, day.

In the changing-room there is a euphoric atmosphere. The team have just won against Arsenal. There is much merriment, noise, singing, chanting, etc. to be heard in the background. Two young footballers, under eighteen, members of the Chelsea Youth Team, are sitting on a bench, chatting about the game. Both are clad in towels, changing after a shower. After a second another player enters, clad in a towel, and makes his way over to the other young players. As he approaches one of the other players picks up an item of clothing and flicks it towards the approaching player. The approaching player retreats and …

Player Oi, watch out. That hurts.

1st boy (*Taking mickey.*) Ahh!

He then throws the item of clothing down. The other player sits and proceeds to dry himself. Mark walks in slowly pushing Robert with Steve. Steve still in kit is very muddy.

Steve Yeah you're right. That ref was a right dickhead. No way was that goal out.

Robert and Mark shake their heads in agreement.

Robert But at least your goal got us the win we deserve.

Steve Yeah, but we should have won by two.

As they reach centre stage there is a chant of praise for Steve.

Well done! Great goal, Steve!

Steve Cheers.

1st boy Hello Rob, good to see ya –

2nd boy Yeah, good to see ya again, Rob –

Robert Gary, Neil –

Gary Great goal by Steve, eh?

Robert Yeah.

Neil How are you then?

Robert Oh not so bad.

Gary When you gonna be up and walking again?

Robert Doctor says it won't be long, about a month.

Neil You'll be back in the team by the end of the season then, eh?

Robert Hang on. Gotta get myself fit again haven't I. Been sitting around for two months. Gotta catch up with you lot. (*They both laugh.*) I'm working on it though. I have to go up to hospital a couple of times a week, for physio. There's this physio there, cor, you should see her. She's beautiful. Swedish.

All listen, interested.

Gary Yeah?

Robert Yeah. She works on my legs. Goes up one leg, hangs about a bit, then goes down the other – the relief's tremendous – know what I mean?

Laughter and disbelief.

Neil Nah. Pull the other one, Rob.

Robert No, that's what she does.

Gary Liar.

Robert (*Aimed at Mark.*) Yeah. That's right, I'm lying. (*Mark moves off to a corner of the stage.*) But I'll be playing again next season though. That's if John'll have me.

Neil Course he'll have you. We need you.

Gary Yeah, course we do. Steve's OK, but you're better.

Neil Besides, Steve's getting too big-headed.

Laughter.

Steve Oi! Watch it!

Robert No. It was a really nice one –

Steve Ta.

Robert You're gonna become a right little Kerry Dixon. You'll soon be in the first team. No hassle.

Steve smiles. Then:

Gary So what you been up to then?

Robert turns to Gary and:

Robert Oh, this and that.

As Robert continues to chat, Steve moves over to Mark. We focus on these two. Mark has just lit up a cigarette and is beginning to smoke it. After a pause:

Steve Thought you'd given that up.

Mark Eh? Oh yeah. So did I. (*Pause.*) Nice goal.

Steve Cheers.

Mark You'll go a long way.

Steve That's what I hope. (*Pause.*) What's up?

Mark Nothing.

Steve Come on. We've known each other longer than that.

Mark What d'you think?

He looks at Steve seriously, takes a deep breath, then:

Steve It's Robert, innit? It's more serious than you've been letting on?

Mark Yeah.

Steve He's not going to get out of the chair is he, let alone play football again.

Mark No.

Steve So what was all that about, all that old chat?

Mark Dunno. (*Pause.*) Think he was having a go at me.

Steve What'd you mean?

Mark Just to show how easy it is.

Steve Easy? What's easy?

Mark Lying.

Steve Lying? What you talking about?

A pause.

Mark Oh, I dunno. I been thinking so much lately it hurts.

Steve Thought that was what college boys was supposed to do. (*Embarrassed.*) Sorry.

Mark It's just been going round and round, in my head, all day long, every day. Whole year it's been going on. 'Spose it was easy at first, when he was still walking, and it was only him and me that knew, and our Dad –

Steve Knew what?

Mark Wearing that silly hat so no one'd know his hair was falling out, still coming down here, chatting with the lads, when he wasn't in hospital. Wearing that silly hat. D'you know every morning there used to be great chunks of hair on the pillow. And now – and now he's in a wheelchair and we've still got to pretend, make out everything's all right. The only person that knows the truth apart from me and Dad is sodding Bryan Robson.

Steve (*Confused.*) Bryan Robson?

Mark He's got secondaries, Steve.

Steve What's that then?

Mark Secondary cancer. Means they can't do anything else. Can't do nothing. I don't know how long he's got – no one does – except he hasn't got long. Few months, a year. I dunno.

A pause.

Steve (*Shocked.*) Oh Jesus, Mark. I never realised. I knew it must be something serious, but ...

Mark Yeah. (*Pause.*) Whole year I've had, telling you lot he's OK, bringing him down sometimes, when he was walking, making out everything was normal ... it was just a minor thing he had wrong with him ... putting a brave face on it. Then we'd go home and I wouldn't have to pretend any more and he wouldn't pretend any more either and, you know, sometimes – he'd scream because of the pain. Now, they've given him this little machine, this little electrical thing, he keeps it in his pocket, he's got it with him now, hides it in his pocket, it's attached to his neck, he twists this knob, it gives him a kinda electric shock, and that eases it, the pain, not much, but a bit. He's in there now, talking about playing again and he's in pain, pain like you and me have never felt. He has to take pills for it too. D'you know how many pills he has to take? Eight pills every four hours, for the pain, and because he feels sick all the time. He doesn't eat. And he's wasting away. And I have to watch it, Steve. Sometimes I sit there and I can't say nothing, not really, I don't know what to say. It's like he's – waiting for me to say something, know what I mean, something that'll take away the pain. What can you say? Eh? You can't say 'Hey Rob, everything's gonna be all right', can you? (*Pause.*) He didn't want to come down here with me this morning. He said he didn't feel well, but really he just didn't want to be seen down here, in the wheelchair. 'Spose he was frightened of blowing the bluff, frightened that people would put two and two together, realise the truth. Can understand, now. D'you know what, I actually told him to sod off. I said 'sod off, Rob, look after yourself'. Can you believe that? And he was lying there and all the time it's getting closer. Every day. It's like lying in bed waiting for the alarm clock to go off ...

A pause then ... from behind them:

Robert Oi, you two. (*Slightly startled they both turn round to Robert. Robert is now sitting alone. To Steve*:) Are you gonna have your shower?

Steve Yeah, of course. It'll only take me a few seconds anyway.

Robert On our way out, would it be all right to go out on to the pitch?

Steve Yeah, sure. As long as the groundsman isn't watching. Nah, course it'll be all right. Then, maybe we could all go down the pub, have a few pints and a chat over old times, eh? (*Mark and Robert nod.*) Great. Anyway, won't be long.

He takes off his top and throws it down onto the bench then dashes off-stage. There is a pause then:

Mark (*Patting abdomen.*) I'll just go and tell 'em we're about ready.

Mark leaves stage. Robert is alone. There is silence. Robert looks around. He then picks up Steve's Chelsea top, stares at it for a few seconds then places it to his nose and inhales it, taking in all the sweat and toil. Evidence of ninety minutes' hard play.

Scene Eleven

Chelsea F.C. exterior ground.

Robert and Mark stand silently centre stage drenched in a pool of light, Robert gazes round thoughtfully. After a few seconds Steve, carrying a sports bag, rushes over to them.

Steve Sorry to have kept you waiting.

Robert Oh no trouble. (*He continues his gaze.*)

Steve (*Catching on to his gaze.*) Great ground, isn't it.

Robert Yeah.

Steve Must bring back quite a few good memories.

Robert Not half. The bridge is almost like a second home to me. (*To Mark.*) D'you remember that first ever match you brought me to here?

Mark (*Smiling.*) Do I? He was only inches high and I had him up on me shoulders and he was cheering his head off for Chelsea and we were surrounded by all these Spurs supporters. We were really lucky. I thought we were gonna get a right clobbering.

Robert Good match though, eh? John was playing then. He scored a penalty that was our one and only home win that season. That was the day I realised all I ever wanted to do was play football, and for Chelsea.

Steve D'you remember that first ever reserve game we both played? Night game. Against West Ham.

Robert (*Smiling.*) Yeah. I remember both sitting in the dressing-room, shit scared of going out. Then the bell went, we ran up the tunnel and the crowd really hit ya. It was like thousands of faces and arms, all cheering. It made all the nerves go and it made ya just wanna get out there and give it all you got. It was a great day.

Steve And you scored a great goal.

Robert Yeah. Most of all, I can still remember the noise, noise of the crowd when I scored. It was as if the world cheered. Maybe they weren't really there, after all it was only a reserve game. Anyway it was dark, couldn't see behind the lights. But for the first time in my life, I felt important. (*Pause.*) But I 'spose even greater than that for me, was afterwards. Actually being signed as a Chelsea apprentice. Oh, I know it isn't very glamorous. Most of the time we spent training or cleaning other players' boots, but at long last I could actually say that I was part of Chelsea Football Club. Meant I could train with players like Alan Hudson, John, people that I only read about in the paper. (*Pause.*) Help me up, lads, would ya?

Mark and Steve *(Together.) What?*

Robert Help me stand up, will you?

Steve and Mark look at each other then they both lean down and help Robert stand up one under each arm. Robert takes it in for a few seconds then:

D'you know what? Sounds really silly now, but every night after training I used to run up the tunnel, trying to remember that crowd, and all those cheering arms and faces, and pretend that I was going out in the first team for Chelsea. It was more than just a dream ...

There is a few seconds silence then Robert starts to sink down.

OK.

Both lads ease him down. Mark puts the footplates back as, to Steve:

OK then. What about this drink?

Steve (*Smiling.*) Right. (*They then walk off-stage.*)

Scene Twelve

Casualty cubicle, interior, night.

In the background, noise of hospital life going on all around. The distant echoing noises of voices, clattering trolleys, etc. Robert is lying on a bed, holding his stomach, in some pain. Mark is pacing. After a few seconds Robert cries out. Mark rushes over to him.

Mark Rob –

Robert (*Turning.*) It's just so painful. I want to go so badly, but I just can't.

Mark Don't worry. The doctor'll be here in a minute.

Robert (*Still moaning.*) Uugher.

A nurse enters, pushing a trolley.

Nurse (*To Mark.*) The doctor's on his way.

The nurse then moves the trolley to the bottom of the bed, and starts arranging things, ready for the doctor.

Mark (*To Robert.*) The doctor's just coming, Rob.

Robert groans again. After a few seconds a young doctor, very sure of himself, enters.

Doctor Sorry to have kept you waiting. I've just been having a look through Robert's notes. It's a very interesting case. (*The doctor moves closer to Robert.*) Now what seems to be the trouble? The nurse tells me you can't pass urine, is that right?

Robert Yeah.

Doctor When was the last time you went?

Robert Er, last night. I wanted to go this morning when I got up, but I couldn't and I've been wanting to go all day. I feel that I wanna go, but I just can't.

Doctor Let me have a feel of your stomach.

He rolls Robert's jumper up and places his hand on to his abdomen. Robert reacts violently.

Does that hurt?

Robert (*Groaning.*) Yeah.

The doctor continues to examine the abdomen carefully.

Doctor Mmm. It is very distended. All right. (*He rolls the jumper down.*) What I'm going to have to do is put a catheter in. Have you ever had a catheter before?

Robert No.

Doctor Well all it is is a thin tube which will pass through your penis and into your bladder to drain off all the fluid that's there.

Robert That sounds painful.

Doctor I'm afraid it is a bit, but there's no other way. Anyway I'll try and be as gentle as I can. All right? (*Robert groans. To nurse.*) Is the trolley ready?

Nurse Yes.

The doctor then turns to Mark.

Doctor If you could wait outside for a minute.

Mark Well I'd rather stay.

Nurse It would be easier if you stayed outside. (*The nurse then moves over to Mark and gently ushers him off to the edge of the stage.*) I'll give you a call as soon as we've finished. We won't be long.

The nurse then walks back to the trolley and starts preparing things ready for the doctor, getting the instruments ready, taking gloves out of a packet, etc. The doctor, out of view, washes his hands thoroughly. Robert waits in the midst of all this. As this is happening, Mark, edge of stage, starts pacing. He then takes out a packet of cigarettes and proceeds to light one. After washing his hands, the doctor then walks over to the nurse, both forearms held up in front of him. The nurse then takes some gloves, holding then, touching them as little as possible, and places them on the doctor's hands. He then moves over to Robert.

Doctor OK?

Robert Yeah.

The nurse then hands the doctor a paper towel with a hole in the middle. The doctor takes it over Robert's lower half. The nurse then picks up a bowl containing antiseptic fluid and a piece of cotton wool. She then hands the cotton wool to the doctor. He takes the cotton wool, rips a small piece off and:

Doctor I'm just going to give a little wash below – make sure everything's clean.

He dips a piece of cotton wool into the bowl and then proceeds to clean Robert's lower half. He disposes of the damp piece of cotton wool into the bowl and then dries the area off with the clean piece of cotton wool which he then also disposes of into the bowl. The nurse places the bowl back on to the trolley. She then hands him a small tube with a nozzle on it.

This is some anaesthetic gel. It'll feel a bit cold.

He continues the operation, all out of vision as he squeezes some gel into the tip of Robert's penis. Robert reacts to the cold.

Cold?

Robert Yeah. (*The doctor then hands the tube back to the nurse who places it back on to the trolley.*)

Nurse What size catheter do you want?

Doctor Er, I think a size 16.

The nurse then glances through a selection of catheters on the trolley and takes out the appropriate one. She opens the top of the sealed catheter then holds it out to the doctor. He takes hold of the top of the catheter as the nurse pulls the wrapping away from it, disposing of it in a paper bag on the side of the trolley. The doctor holds the catheter.

I'm just going to insert the catheter now, alright?

Robert nods

So try and relax.

There is a pause, then the doctor out of vision begins to insert the catheter. Robert screams out in pain. Mark, side of stage, who is pacing, stops, shocked, as he hears Robert. Robert screams out again. Mark rushes over to Robert.

Just try and relax. Take deep breaths. In. And out.

The doctor, concentrating hard on inserting the catheter, turns slightly as Mark approaches.

Everything's all right, if you could just wait outside … (*To Robert.*) Relax now. Deep breaths. Deep breaths. In. And out. In. And out.

Robert tries hard. He calms down, taking short sharp breaths, crying out periodically as the pain of the catheterisation impinges. All this as the nurse gently pushes Mark off to the side of the stage.

Nurse It would be much easier if you could wait outside. Everything's fully under control and we'll let you know as soon as we're finished.

The nurse rushes back to the trolley leaving Mark defeated and helpless. The doctor is still continuing to encourage Robert who is trying to relax. After a few seconds:

Doctor All right. The catheter's in now.

Robert gives a loud sigh. The nurse then passes a kidney-shaped dish in which is a small syringe to the doctor. The doctor takes out the small syringe and again out of vision injects it down below. The doctor then disposes of the syringe back into the kidney-shaped dish which the nurse places back on to the trolley. She then hands the doctor a urine drainage bag which the doctor takes and then connects to the catheter. He places it down by his side and looks down at the bag after a few seconds.

That's beginning to drain now. Yes. (*To Robert.*) How's that feel?

Robert I still feel like there's a lot there.

Doctor Yes. I think it's going to take a while to empty completely. But I'll let it drain and then come back and see how your bladder is in a bit. All right? (*Robert nods.*) Good. Thank you nurse.

The doctor then walks off-stage, removing his gloves.

Nurse (*To Robert.*) I'll get your brother for you.

She exits pushing the trolley. To Mark.

You can go in now.

Slowly Mark walks over to Robert. Robert is recovering exhausted. There is an uneasy silence.

Mark (*Quietly.*) Cor, bet that bloody hurt, didn't it?

Robert Mmmm.

Mark (*Moving in closer.*) Made my nuts tighten up just thinking about it. (*He looks down at the bag.*) At least you're going now anyway. How does it feel?

Robert Much better. (*There is a pause then:*)

Mark Well, I've heard of going out on the piss, but this is taking it. (*Robert laughs, weakly.*)

Robert Don't make me laugh, it's too painful.

Scene Thirteen

A blank space, dimly lit from one corner, a blue rippling light glows down the front. Background noise of water, gently rippling by and distant noises of a city asleep, traffic moving by, the odd shout of a person and the occasional bark of a dog, etc. Robert and Mark, both wearing coats, wrapped up warm, move slowly into the centre of the stage.

Robert Mark, can we stop here a minute? (*Mark stops.*)

Mark (*Puzzled.*) Yeah, sure. (*Robert gazes up and around, smiling.*)

Robert Beautiful, innit? The moon up there. Cool breeze. (*Snapping out of his gaze.*) Bet that sounds bloody silly, doesn't it? But you never stop to think how great things are. (*Mark crouches down to Robert's level.*)

Mark (*Gazing around.*) No, you're right there. You take so much for granted.

Robert I've always loved the night time. If ever I 'ad any problems, I'd wait till the night time, then I'd sit up in bed or go for a long walk to think things through. Sometimes I'd even come down here. Everything's so much more peaceful and calm. It's as if the world slows down to give you a chance to sort everything out, before it starts up again the next morning. (*Pause.*) Do you believe in God?

Mark I dunno. I believe in something. But what I'm not sure.

Robert I do. It was just after that old bloke died, the one opposite me in the 'ospital, d'you remember? He had the same routine every day. He'd have a cup of tea when it came round at six, go to the bathroom, come out, read the paper, have his breakfast, then wait to go down for his treatment. After lunch he'd always have a little kip then he'd come over and chat to me. He was a nice old bloke. He'd worked for the same firm, in the same office, for forty-five years. He'd just retired. Never had a day's illness in his life, before then. One night I woke up and his curtains were round and his light was on. There was a lot of noise and doctors and nurses going in and out. The next morning his bed was empty. I knew what had happened. I thought, there was a man who saw the same people, did the same things, day in, day out. Then one night, that was it. All over. That's when I decided that there must be more to it than that. There must be more to it than that, hey, Mark? I'm not sure what. Maybe you come back as something else in another life. Who knows, I might come back as some great player for Chelsea. Knowing my luck though, I'll probably come back playing for Fulham. (*They both laugh. There is a pause. Then Robert sighs and tuts.*) Oh I wish ... I just wish that I'd done more.

Mark Don't talk like that. Doctors aren't always right. You've got to think positive.

A pause.

Robert D'you know one thing I wish I'd done? (*Pause.*) I wish that I'd got some girl pregnant. So that she could have my child. A boy. Something that I'd created. God knows I 'ad the opportunities, but I was always trying to avoid it. The one thing I hope we'd have would be a real family. A proper mum and dad. (*Pause.*) It's funny, I can't remember what Mum looked like. It's as if she never existed. You've never talked about her either.

Mark I can't remember much about her either. It was a bit like your old man really. One morning I woke up, and she wasn't there any more. I was told that Mum had been in an accident and that she wouldn't be coming home. Didn't really understand at the time. God I was only six, you were only four. Wasn't till much later, that I realised.

Robert Do you think Dad loved her?

Mark Course he did. If he didn't he'd have married someone else.

Robert Except who'd have him? (*They laugh.*) D'you think he ever said it though?

Mark Said? Said what?

Robert Told her he loved her. Said 'I love you'.

Mark Must have done, I 'spose. Can't imagine him proposing though, can you? (*They both laugh*). Down on one knee and all that. (*They both laugh again. There is a pause.*)

Robert D'you think Dad loves us?

Mark Well yes, of course. Oh, I know he doesn't show it much, but that's just the way he is. Maybe thinks it's pouffy or something, I dunno. Anyhow, he does love us.

Robert Have I ever said it to you?

Mark What?

Robert That I love you.

Mark Dunno. Can't remember.

Robert Don't think I have. (*He looks at Mark.*) I love you Mark. (*A slight pause.*)

Mark I love you too, Rob. (*A slight pause.*)

Robert Hug me then, would you, please? (*Mark moves closer* *and puts his arms around Robert. After a few seconds.*)

Mark 'Ere, we'd better get going. It's all right for you, I've got college in the morning. (*He then pushes Robert slowly off-stage.*)

Scene Fourteen

Kitchen, interior, morning.

Mark is sitting at the table, having finished his breakfast, reading a book. After a few seconds the father, much the worse for wear from the previous night's drinking, enters ready for work.

Father Morning. (*Father sits as Mark glances up from his book.*)

Mark (*Dismissively.*) Morning.

Father then pours himself out a cup of tea. After a pause.

You seen Robert this morning?

Father No. I looked in, he was fast alseep.

Mark Well he would be. He happened to have a very rough night last night.

Father Yeah. Me too.

Mark (*Angrily.*) Yeah? We were both at the hospital till gone two.

Father What?

Mark He couldn't pee. They had to stick some tube in him to get it all out. I tried to wake you before we went but you were too pissed out of your mind.

Father (*Defiantly.*) What?

Mark The other night I thought maybe I'd got through to you but I must have been stupid – on the way back from the hospital Robert asked me if I thought you loved him. I said yes of course you did, but I wonder, I wonder whether you really do. We could both drop down dead tomorrow and you wouldn't even notice. In fact I don't think you give a toss about either of us.

Father (*Jumps up, lashing out.*) Oi! Watch it!

Mark (*Jumps up, shouting.*) Go on then! Hit me! That's gonna make everything better, innit. Go on, hit me. Hit me. And find out how hard I can hit back.

The father recoils. A silent pause. Mark fills a Chelsea F.C. mug with tea, then adds milk and sugar. The father stands in silence. Mark slides the mug nearer to his father.

Here. If you want to make things better, why don't you take this in to him.

The father looks down at the mug then slowly picks it up, then walks off stage. Mark gives a loud sigh. Then sits, exhausted.

Scene Fifteen

Robert and Mark's bedroom, interior, morning.

The room is darkened. Robert is lying in bed, his eyes closed. After a few seconds the father enters with the tea. He walks, slowly, over to Robert. He then squats down and looks at Robert. After a silence, Robert stirs.

Robert (*Surprised.*) Hello.

Father (*Hesitant.*) Morning. I called in earlier but you were asleep. Brought you your tea.

He holds out the mug. Robert takes the mug and puts his hand around it.

Robert Ta. I'll need a straw though, Mark keeps them over there, in that jar. (*The father rises and looks round.*) On the cupboard.

The father moves to the cupboard and takes a straw from the jar.

Father I hear you had some problems last night.

Robert Yeah.

The father moves back to Robert and hands him the straw.

Father All right now is it?

Robert Think so.

The father crouches down beside Robert again. There is an uneasy pause.

Father Your brother finishes college today.

Robert Yeah.

Father Be nice to have him home, eh?

Robert Yeah. (*Robert sips his tea. Another pause.*)

Father Robert. You do realise, I love you, don't you? I've always tried to give you everything I never had when I was a kid. (*Pause.*) I've been saving up some money. I've got four hundred quid and some overtime to come, too. Thought we might be able to go somewhere, get away, abroad, if you like. Just the three of us. Been a long time since we've done anything like that, eh? Anywhere in particular you fancy going?

Robert (*Thinks.*) I've always wanted to see the Bernebau Stadium in Spain. Some of me mates have been, they say it's really good.

A pause.

Father (*Rising.*) Right. I'll pop into that travel place on my way home from work, pick up some brochures. Maybe we can look at them together tomorrow.

Robert Yeah.

Father Right. (*Another pause.*) I'm late already. I'd better be off. (*He goes to walk off-stage then stops, his back towards Robert. Awkwardly.*) Your mother. When she was killed in that crash, I couldn't handle it. Still can't.

Robert Yeah, I understand. (*The father glances back at Robert briefly. Then goes.*)

Scene Sixteen

Chelsea dressing-room, interior, day.

Noisy, boisterous, atmosphere, players getting changed, etc. Dave dressed in full kit is sitting on the bench. He is bent over tying up his bootlace. As he sits up he grimaces and holds his groin. Steve, also dressed in full kit, enters from off-stage, carrying his boots. He notices Dave's hand on his groin.

Steve Groin playing you up again, eh?

Dave Just a bit.

Steve sits next to Dave placing his boots on the ground.

Steve You ought to get that seen to, if it is a groin strain you should be off resting it.

Dave Won't have much chance of getting into the first team if I'm off will I?

Steve If it's a strain and you aggravate it you'll have even less chance.

Dave Oh, it's not that bad.

Steve I had a bad strain once and it was only by resting it that it got better.

Dave Yeah, I know, but it might not be anything to do with football.

Steve Oh. (*Smiles.*) It doesn't matter how you got the strain it's what you do with it when you've got it.

Dave (*Unconvinced.*) Yeah. (*Steve shakes his head and tuts. Dave rises and start to work out.*) Anyway once I'm on the move it's OK.

Steve then bends down and puts his boots on as Dave continues working out. After tying his boots, Steve looks up. He notices a young boy, Gary, sixteen, dressed in casual clothes and carrying a sports bag who looks lost.

Steve (*Calling out.*) Are you looking for someone, mate?

The boy moves over to Steve and Dave.

Gary Yeah, someone called Steve.

Steve I'm Steve.

Gary Gwyn told me to look out for you. My name's Gary. I've got a trial this afternoon.

Steve holds out his hand.

Steve Nice to meet ya. (*They shake hands. Pointing.*) This is Dave.

Dave nods and smiles. Gary smiles back. Dave sits again.

So this is your first trial?

Gary Yeah. I got another one for Fulham for exactly the same time, but I chose this one cos I've always wanted to play for Chelsea.

Steve So where've you been playing then?

Gary Oh, just junior ones, school, district and for my county. I got spotted at one of the school games.

Steve Oh, so you're the new find he's been going on about. Four goals in your last two games. (*Gary smiles, embarrassed.*) Welcome to Chelsea, my son. We need more people like you.

Gary Hopeful thinking. I'm only here for a trial. How long you been an apprentice then?

Steve (*Thinking.*) Just over a year. 'Spose.

Gary Oh, it must be great, eh?

Steve Well, I don't know about that – it's a lot of hard work.

Gary Yeah, I know, but it must be nice to feel part of a team.

Steve Yeah, it's nice to come down here and train with the others, gives you an incentive to really work hard and they're a good lot. And if you've worked hard enough at the end of the week you'll feel just that bit nearer the first team.

Steve and Gary smile.

Dave Also if you just mention you're a footballer at Chelsea you'll have no trouble pulling the birds, they'll be all over you.

Steve There speaks Chelsea's answer to the 'American Gigolo'.

Steve and Dave laugh.

Gary Oh, yeah. In all the excitement I forgot me boots, Gwyn said I'd be able to borrow a pair.

Steve Yeah, sure. What size d'you take?

Gary Ten.

Steve Have a look down there Dave – there should be some down there ...

Dave turns and looks behind him. He finds a shoe, and:

Dave (*Turning.*) There. (*Holding them up.*) Size ten.

Steve Great.

Dave spots something and:

Dave (*Holding back.*) Hold on. They're Robert's ...

There is a pause.

Steve Well, they've seen some action, they might as well be put to some good use.

He takes the boots and hands them to Gary.

Gary Cheers.

A bell sounds followed by an off-stage voice.

Voice (*'HI-DE-HI' Accent.*) Good afternoon, players. Could you all retire ... oh ... to the pitch where your camp coach awaits. (*There is a raucous roar from the stage...*) for this week's nobbly knee competition. (*Normal.*) And for those of you who don't speak Welsh. 'Get your lazy backsides out of here and on to the pitch, training has begun ...'

Dave I think that means us.

Steve Mmmm. (*Dave rises followed by Steve. The stage then begins to empty of players.*) If you want to change here you can leave your gear with ours, nobody'll touch it ...

Gary Oh thanks.

Steve See you out there then.

Dave Yeah.

Gary Right, thanks again.

Steve and Dave move off-stage. The stage empties completely. Steve gives two loud, exaggerated claps. Gary looks up, slightly startled.

Steve (*Moving in.*) Not bad. (*Gary looks down, embarrassed.*) How about helping us score a few goals outside, eh?

Gary (*Smiling.*) Right.

The two then move off-stage.

Steve I'll race you ...

Steve rushes off.

Gary Hold on ...

Gary follows.

Scene Seventeen

Hospital, corridor, night.

Mark, shocked, walks slowly out on to a dimly lit stage and sits on a wooden bench. In the background the noise of hospital life going on, doctors being paged, the clattering of trolleys and the distant 'echoey' noises of voices (as in Scene Two). Mark sits, still and silent. After a few seconds his father rushes on stage, a little out of breath. He is carrying a pile of holiday brochures.

Father Hello son, how's Rob? I just got a call at work saying he'd been taken into hospital, see. Is it something to do with his bladder again? (*There is no response from Mark.*) Well son? How is he?

Mark, now straining to hold back the tears.

Mark It's too late Dad. He, he's dead.

The father takes a few seconds to take it in, then:

Father No. No, he can't be. I've got these brochures from the travel place. He said he wanted to go to Spain. We're going to look through them together tonight.

Mark (*Rising.*) Well it's too late now.

Suddenly the reality of the situation hits the father. He starts to lose control of his emotions and begins to drop several brochures. Mark, slowly, crouches down and picks up the brochures. He rises and after a slight hesitation, he puts his arm round his father. After a few seconds they both embrace and we can hear the sound of tears from both. After a long pause:

Mark Come on Dad. Let's go home.

The two then walk, slowly, off-stage …

(Suggest that as the two walk slowly off-stage we hear the sound of the Chelsea apprentices training (as in previous scene). Fading out into the distance to the Chelsea theme tune: 'Blue is the colour, Chelsea is our name'.)

Curtain

Lives Worth Living

Lawrence Evans and Jane Nash

CASTS OF THE FIRST PERFORMANCES

Cast of first tour

The programme was researched and devised by Lawrence Evans and Jane Nash. It was first performed in June 1983.

Mark Sutton................................Lawrence Evans
Julie Sutton ....Jane Nash
Designed by ....Lawrence Evans/Jane Nash/
Elliott Grey Turner
Publicity/schools' liaison........Adrienne Benham

Cast of second tour

The programme was re-toured in May 1984.

A performance was requested by the Arts Council of Great Britain for their National Conference on Theatre and Education held at the University of Warwick, 20–22 July 1984.

Mark Sutton................................Lawrence Evans
Julie Sutton ....Gill Nathanson

AUTHOR'S NOTE

Our aims

The aim of the piece was to confront people's own prejudice, fear and ignorance about mental handicap.

To show internal and external pressures placed on a family where one or more members are mentally handicapped.

To examine the stereotypical role of women as carers within our society.

To show that mentally handicapped people are people first.

What happens to mentally handicapped young people after they leave school?

Although the Company worked with mentally handicapped children it had never really considered this question until it was raised at an ideas meeting for future in-school programmes. From that initial question, the Company decided to devise a programme aimed at mid-secondary students about adult mental handicap.

In order to do justice to a group of people who are neglected and rejected by our society (through society's fear and ignorance), we decided in our research to cover as many aspects of mental handicap as we could. We felt the best way of doing this was by getting as much firsthand experience as possible.

We began by contacting MENCAP (Royal Society for Mentally Handicapped Children and Adults) and several voluntary organisations involved with the mentally handicapped. None more so than Coventry Social Services Department (with its specialist group of social workers for mentally handicapped people) whose help was invaluable.

At the end of our research period, we had amassed many hours of taped interviews with nurses, doctors, social workers, teachers, staff of Industrial Therapy Units, Day Care Centres, Hostels and Residential Homes. The main bulk of our interviews however were with mentally handicapped people themselves and their families. Every family we met, shared with us their personal and intimate experience of mental handicap and without their complete openness, this play could not have been written.

It is to those people we owe our gratitude in our attempt to show and raise questions about the way we, as a society, treat mentally handicapped people and their families.

What we both learnt from our research was that it is a constant fight for mentally handicapped people to be recognised as people first and that their biggest handicap is other people's attitudes.

Lawrence Evans and Jane Nash

THE CHARACTERS

Julie Sutton is 23 years old. She is an unemployed nursery nurse. It is important that she is somewhat unconventional. In the original production she was fashion-conscious with blue hair and very 'loud' taste in clothes!

This was for several reasons:

To show her as a part of society also pre-judged and looked down upon.

To smash any assumptions/value judgements the audience may have made about her from her appearance alone.

To show that carers can be non-conformists and non-conformists can be carers.

Mark Sutton is 22 years old. He is mentally handicapped. In the original production he had athetoid movements of one arm (involuntary muscle spasms). He walked with a slightly spastic gait and he had involuntary tongue movements called Tongue Thrust. (He stuck his tongue out in a downward motion.) He also spoke very loudly. There were several reasons for playing the role of Mark in this way:

To give the actor a 'hook'/a way to the character.

To confront the audience with a stereotypical image of a mentally handicapped person.

Family background

John Sutton married Mary Carr when he was 22 and she was 20. Mary was three months' pregnant with her daughter Julie. Eleven months after Julie's birth, Mark was born.

John Sutton left home when Mark and Julie were three and four respectively and some years later, John and Mary were divorced. Mark and Julie started off at the same primary school. After a year and following an assessment, Mark was moved to an Educationally Sub-Normal School (Moderate). After another year and further assessment, he was moved out of the education system and into a Junior Training Centre run by the Health Authority. In 1971, the Education Act stated that mentally handicapped people were now educable and that their schooling should be placed under the control of the Education Authority rather than the Health Authority. Consequently, the Junior Training Centre which Mark was attending became a Special School where Mark stayed until he was eighteen years old.

When Mark was fourteen he went into a mental subnormality hospital for three months while his mother recovered from nervous exhaustion.

Mary Sutton died of cancer at the age of 42 after a long illness – one month before the action of the play.

The set

The set comprised:

A sand-coloured carpet 16 feet by 14 feet

9 yellow cubes 1½ feet square

A collection of yellow building bricks – various sizes

The carpet represents the beach, the yellow cubes represent rocks and the building bricks are used to make a sandcastle.

Lawrence Evans and Jane Nash

LIVES WORTH LIVING

The action of the play takes place on a beach in Southend.

Taped voices off: The sound of the pop song 'Under attack' *by* Abba *is heard playing. Noise of seagulls and waves can also be heard. After some time:*

Voice 1 (*Off.*) Hey look at him over there. Here you, Oi!

Voice 1 and 3 (*Off.*) Oi!

Voice 2 (*Off.*) Oi you!

Voice 1 (*Off.*) Hey, hey come on. Look at me. Here you, look at me. Look at me will yer!

Voice 3 (*Off.*) We're talking to you!

Voice 2 (*Off.*) Come on.

Voice 3 (*Off.*) Come on then.

Voice 2 (*Off.*) Come on!

Voice 1 (*Off.*) Oi mental!

Voice 3 (*Off.*) Funny in the 'ead.

Voice 2 (*Off.*) Spazzo.

Laughter, voice 1 begins a song to the tune of the conga. Voices 2 and 3 join in.

Voice 1 (*Off.*) Let's all go to Tescos

Where spazzies get their best clothes.

A spazzy mong, a spazzy mong.

Let's all go to Tescos

Where spazzies get their best clothes

A spazzy mong, spazzy mong …

Voice 3 (*Laughing.*) Oi look at his face!

Voice 4 (*Laughing.*) Yeah. Who let you out eh?

Laughter from voices 1, 2 and 3. The voices fade away leaving the sound of 'Under attack' *by* Abba *still playing.*

Julie (*Angrily from off stage.*) Mark, come here. Come here!

Enter Julie wearing sunglasses and carrying a deck-chair, picnic bag, beach sandals, a plastic 'Superman' handbag and a carrier bag. Mark follows behind wearing sunglasses and carrying a beach umbrella, a ball, bucket, spade and a Tesco's carrier bag in one hand and a stereo cassette recorder with the song 'Under attack' *by* Abba *in the other. Julie stares at Mark. Mark looks away. Julie is annoyed and throws her belongings down on the beach. Mark copies her action. Julie begins to set up her deck-chair whilst Mark arranges his own things by the side of the rocks. Julie has great difficulty with the deck-chair until totally frustrated, she throws it to the ground and moves away. Mark has noticed this, goes to the deck-chair and with no difficulty, sets up the chair.*

Mark There y'are Julie.

Mark goes over to his Tesco carrier bag, removes a book and offers it to Julie.

Julie Why do you let them get away with it? (*Mark looks away.*) Oh give us me book! (*Julie snatches book off Mark. She sits in deck-chair and reads her book. Mark then begins a series of actions to try and pacify her, all of which fail. He switches off the cassette recorder. He collects the picnic bag and carrier bag and places them by the side of the deck-chair and waits. He picks up her Superman bag and does the same. He notices Julie's beach sandals and places them by her feet. Julie does not react. Giving up, he moves to his own things. Julie watches him. Amazed.*) What are you wearing?

Mark What? (*Pause. Mark laughs by doing a tongue thrust.*) Clothes. Boom! Boom! Beat yer.

Julie Showing me up. Take yer jacket off.

Mark What.

Julie It's hot. You wear cool clothes cos it's hot.

Mark Oh. (*Mark takes off his jacket.*) This? (*Pointing at his slip-over.*)

Julie Yeah. (*Mark tries to take off his slip-over. He gets it half off but becomes stuck. He moves to Julie.*)

Mark Pull. Tar! (*Puts jumper with his jacket.*) There!

Julie Tie.

Mark What? (*She notices his tie and removes it. Julie goes back to her book.*) Shoes and socks?

Julie Yeah go on, live dangerously!

Mark sits and unties laces.

Mark Pull, pull, pull. There! (*He throws the first shoe behind him. He then decides to pull off his second shoe without bothering to untie the laces. He throws the second shoe behind him. He then removes his socks. Gleefully waggling his toes.*) Yeah!

(*Mark then notices that Julie's trousers are rolled up. He does the same to his. Finally notices the audience. Removing his sun-glasses he jumps up and rushes straight to a member of the audience. Holding out his hand.*) Hello! What's your name? ... My name's Mark. How ja do. (*He shakes hands.*) Are you on holiday? I am. We bin here a week. (*He moves to another member of the audience.*) Hello! What's your name? ... My name's Mark. How ja do. (*He shakes hands. Pointing to a third member of the audience.*) You're nice! Yeah. (*He then notices the centre section of the audience and goes over to them.*) Hello, what's your name? ... My name's Mark. How ja do. Do you like dancin'? I do! Julie took me to a disco last week. It was fun. Didn't play no Abba though. They're my favourite! Stay there!! (*He goes over and gets his cassette recorder.*) D' you like it? ... Julie and Trev bought it me. Listen. (*He plays the cassette.* Abba's 'Under attack' *is still playing. Thrusting tongue out gleefully.*) It's Abba! (*Pause.*) Enough! (*He turns off cassette and takes it back. Returning he notices audience on the left and goes over to them.*) Hello.

What's your name? ... My name's Mark. How ja do. (*He shakes hands and moves to someone else.*) Do you go to work? ... I do. I work at the ... Industrial Therapy Unit. Yeah. We do ... light assembly. That's puttin' bits together ... (*He demonstrates*) ... and packagin'. Don't like it. Wanna leave. Be a Mechanic. Yeah! (*He addresses another person in the audience.*) Do you go to school? ... I bin to three schools. They're special. (*To another person, male or female. Adapt lines accordingly.*) You got a boyfriend? I got a girlfriend. She's called Denise. She works at the Centre with me. (*Pointing.*) D' yer fancy him over there? I'll fix yer up if you want.

Throughout this, Julie has ignored what Mark has been doing until she hears him talk about girlfriends/boyfriends. She then looks round to find something to distract him. She notices a shell.

Julie Mark, come and see what I've found.

Mark (*Turning round.*) What?

Julie Come and see!

Mark (*To audience.*) See yer later! (*Mark does a thumbs up sign and goes to Julie.*)

Julie It's a shell!

Mark Cor. Big innit. (*Pause.*)

Julie Can you hear the sea?

Mark (*Ecstatically.*) Yeah! (*Notices starfish.*) Look!

Julie (*Going over to starfish.*) Oh it's a starfish!

Mark Why?

Julie Cos it looks like a star I suppose. (*Julie brings the starfish over to Mark.*) Lovely innit?

Mark (*Warily.*) Yeah.

Julie (*Thrusts it towards Mark's face.*) Touch it.

Mark (*Scared.*) No!

Julie (*With a smile.*) Go on. It won't hurt you.

Mark approaches the starfish with caution and eventually touches it. He screams. Julie laughs.

Mark Stop!!

Julie stops laughing. Mark then attempts to pick up the starfish which he eventually does.

Julie There see. Looks like a star!

Mark (*Still warily.*) Eey' ar!

Julie (*With a smile.*) I'll put it back in the sand. (*She goes and buries the starfish. Mark copies Julie and buries the shell. To audience.*) It's our last day here today.

Mark I don't wanna go tomorrow, Julie.

Julie What d'you mean 'I don't wanna go tomorrow'! How many more times? Now just don't wind me up cos I'm on me holiday, right?

Mark I'm not goin'.

Julie (*Getting annoyed.*) We've been through this, Mark. You're goin' to Northfields!

Mark (*Defiantly.*) I'm not!

Julie (*Brightly.*) You said you wanted to go yesterday. You said it was all right.

Mark I'm not goin'!

Julie What do you think I am?

Mark No!

Julie (*Getting annoyed.*) It wasn't my decision, right. It was you and Mum. You decided.

Mark (*Loudly.*) No!

Julie Well what if I've got used to the idea? What if I want that? What if? Now you just change your bloody mind. Every five minutes. Mum wanted that. She's not here to look after you now ... (*with a sneer*) ... to wash your hair and tie your shoe laces.

Mark (*Petulantly.*) Do it myself.

Julie (*To audience.*) He does this every bloody time. You never know where you are with him. He lead Mum a right dance! Course the best one was when he was gonna start working at the Training Centre ...

Mark begins to rock backwards and forwards on his knees.

Mark (*Interrupting.*) Work's borin'. I hate it.

Julie ... Three weeks before the day he's due to go: 'I'm not goin' there, Mum.' 'You what?' she says. He says: 'I'm not goin'. I don't wanna work somewhere like that.' She was worried sick. Where was he gonna go? Prospective employers weren't exactly falling at his feet! I mean Woolworth's weren't likely to take him on filling bloody shelves!

Mark Work's borin'. I hate it. They say you're easily pleased cos yer can't fink. Don't matter wot yer do s'long as yer busy. Don't treat yer right. 'Fore I came away I was in the office. Stood there, four of 'em. 'What you bin doin' now Mark?' 'I 'ad an argument, sir.' 'Who wiv Mark?' 'Fred, sir.' (*Upset and angry.*) 'He's bin arguin' with everyone. Haven't you Mark?' 'Have to stop your wages so you learn. That's fair innit?'

Julie So it wasn't the best place in the world! But there's no alternative.

Mark 'Now say you're sorry for all the trouble.'

Julie Come the day he's due to go. He walks out happy as larry onto the bus!

Julie (*Remembering.*) 'Sorry.'

Julie (*To Mark.*) Mum's bin sweatin' for three weeks.

Mark (*Angrily.*) 'And in front of visitors an' all.'

Julie (*To Mark. Firmly.*) You're not doin' that to me y'know!

Mark (*Looking at Julie.*) What? (*He turns away. Pause.*) What? (*He feels his head and looks up at the sky. He smells his hand and then looks up pointing ...*) Julie, that seagull's just shit on my head.

Julie (*Aside.*) Why don't you say it louder so the whole beach can hear.

Mark (*Shouts.*) That seagull's just shit on my head!

Julie (*Shouts.*) Come here!

Mark (*Showing her his hand.*) Look!

Julie (*Taking his hand.*) Tut! Show us yer head! Tut! Oh come on we'll have to wash it out. (*Julie takes Mark by the hand, climbs over the rocks and goes to the sea. She removes her shoes and jumps in. Mark stares at the waves.*) Ooooh ... it's freezing! Come on! (*Mark backs away.*) Come on.

Mark (*Frightened.*) No!

Julie I can't do it from there can I?

Mark No!

Julie Come on. (*Mark builds himself up to jump. When he enters the sea, he screams. Julie laughs.*)

Mark Stop!

Julie (*Laughing.*) Do your hand. (*Julie mimes washing Mark's head. Mark washes his hand.*) Trust you! (*She continues washing his head.*) There! (*Mark mimes scooping water to throw at Julie and laughs at the same time.*) You dare! (*Mark laughs again.*) I'm warnin' you! (*Mark splashes at Julie.*) Oh you so and so! Right! (*Julie splashes Mark using her feet.*)

Mark (*Laughing.*) *Julie and Mark kick water at each other.*) I give in! I give in! I'm all wet now!

Julie Serves you right, you started it!

Mark What?

Julie (*With affection.*) You hungry?

Mark Yeah!

Julie Come on then.

Julie comes out of the sea, collects her shoes and goes back to the deck-chair. Mark jumps out of the sea, takes a quick look back at the water and follows. Julie unzips the picnic bag and hands Mark a small table-cloth.

Julie Here y' are!

Mark Tar!

Whilst unpacking the rest of the picnic, Julie watches Mark to see if he can cope with laying out the table-cloth. Mark spreads out the cloth, meticulously smoothing out the creases. He then gets up and walks over the cloth back to Julie.

Julie Grab the plates. (*Julie takes the paper cups, sandwich box and packet of biscuits and lays them on the table-cloth. Mark grabs the plates and follows. They both sit. Julie opens the sandwich box and unwraps the sandwiches. Mark waits expectantly.*) It's egg mayonnaise ... (*Mark inspects the sandwich*) ... now don't say you don't like it 'cos I know you do.

Mark All right. (*He looks at Julie's sandwich.*) Wot you got?

Julie Same as you! There's a bottle of lemonade in the bag.

Mark What? (*Mark goes to the picnic bag. He unzips bag and takes out lemonade bottle. N.B. It is important that the picnic bag has a zip to show that Mark is capable of coping with zips.*) Any crisps?

Julie No.

Mark (*Horrified.*) No crisps?!

Julie No crisps.

Mark Why?!

Julie (*Sarcastically.*) Oh I'm terribly sorry. It must have slipped my mind. Would you like me to run to the shops now and get them?

Mark Yeah!

Julie Well you can whistle!

Mark (*Pause. Mark whistles.*) Boom! Boom! Beat yer!

Julie is not amused. Mark knows this. He puts down the lemonade bottle, sits and begins to eat. Julie takes lemonade bottle and tries to open it. She can't.

Julie Here do that for us!

Mark (*Takes bottle and opens it. It fizzes.*) Fizz!

Julie Want some lemonade?

Mark Yeah! (*Julie pours lemonade.*) Enough! (*Mark drinks it down in one. Julie pours some for herself. Mark burps. Pause.*) Pardon! (*Long pause. They settle down.*) Why in't Trevor here?

Julie Didn't want him to come. He's workin' anyway.

Mark D' you love Trevor?

Julie Course I do!

Mark You always say you don't cos 'e thinks more of his car then 'e does of you.

Julie You shouldn't listen to private conversations.

Mark Why not? You're shoutin'. I can't stop me ears up! (*They both laugh and enjoy the joke.*) I think 'e does fink more of 'is car. (*Mark laughs. Julie is not amused and turns away. Pause.*) Didn't mean it. Didn't Julie!

Julie S' all right.

Mark Honest. Didn't.

Julie (*Weary.*) I know. (*Pause. To audience.*) He doesn't miss a trick. Mind you he's right. Trevor is car-mad! Well it's his job; he's a mechanic. Makes good money. I'm trained as a Nursery Nurse – passed all me exams with flying colours. Proudest day of Mum's life ...

Mark notices Julie is talking to the audience. He does the same.

Mark (*Interrupting.*) I got a job!

Julie I'm talking! (*Mark grabs his shoes and moves to deck-chair, annoyed. Julie continues talking to audience.*) Proudest day of Mum's life when I come home with me certificate. If she could see me now. I've bin unemployed for eight months. I worked for four years in a local nursery. Same old story though innit ... Government cuts! Lost me job.

Mark pulls on first shoe.

Mark (*Under his breath.*) I got a job.

Julie Don't tell me. Tell them. (*She indicates audience.*)

Mark What? (*Pause.*) I got a job! I'm somebody. It's like Mister Johnson says 'you're worth somethin', you get a wage'.

Julie And what if you didn't have a job. Wouldn't you be worth anything?

Mark What? (*Pause.*) Don't know.

Julie I haven't got a job. I'm still worth something aren't I?

Mark What? Yeah!

Julie It's a lie then innit? Being somebody isn't dependent on havin' a job y'know. (*Pause.*)

Mark What.

Julie (*To audience.*) Course Trevor thinks he's got it sussed: 'Have a baby', he says. Easy as pie innit? 'Give you somethin' to do during the day.' Oh yeah? That'd knock me off the job market for years. Mind you. I would like kids one day but when I'm ready and on my terms.

Mark pulls on his second shoe.

Mark Oi.

Julie You talkin' to me?

Mark When you 'ave babies, what will that make me?

Julie (*Smiling.*) You'll be their uncle.

Mark (*In wonder.*) Uncle!

Julie Uncle Mark!

Mark Will I? (*Excited squeal.*) Uncle Mark!! When you 'avin' one?

Julie (*Smiling in disbelief.*) When I'm ready. Now finish yer sandwich.

Mark Don't want no more.

Julie There's a packet of biscuits here.

Mark What? (*Mark goes over to get biscuits. He shakes the packet so biscuits fall out everywhere on to the cloth. He takes one.*) No crisps! (*He goes to rocks.*)

Julie No crisps!

Mark Cos you forgot.

Julie Cos I forgot!

Mark (*Half under his breath.*) If I forgot all bloody hell would have let fuckin' loose.

Julie (*Shocked.*) What did you say?

Mark Nuffin. Denise had a baby. They took it away. She told me. (*To audience.*) Denise my girlfriend. She works at the Centre packin' nails into plastic bags wiv me. She's thirty-eight.(*Julie lies down.*)

Julie (*Teasing.*) D' you love Denise?

Mark What?

Julie D' you love her? (*Pause.*)

Mark Shut up!

Julie (*With a quick smile.*) Well do you?

Mark Stop! (*Pause. He begins to laugh.*) My friend. (*Julie lies down again. Mark eats his biscuit. He looks around. Finally.*) Wish Mum was 'ere. She'd a liked this place.

Julie Yeah!

Mark (*Excited.*) She'd paddle.

Julie I miss her y'know. (*Pause.*)

Mark (*Becoming upset.*) Miss her.

Julie (*Trying to distract him.*) That time you brought that frog home.

Mark (*Quietly upset.*) What? (*Mark remembers then gets excited.*) She trod on it ... (*Both laughing.*) ... swimming.

Julie On a Thursday.

Mark Yeah!

Julie With a packet of chips afterwards.

Mark Yeah ... cocoa.

Julie Made with milk on Fridays.

Mark Not water.

Julie Yeah.

Mark Mum singing us to sleep.

Julie Oh er ... Edelweiss.

Mark Yeah . . . the pictures.

Julie Popcorn.

Mark Ice-cream.

Julie The Lone Ranger.

Mark (*Shouting at the top of his voice.*) Tonto! ... (*laughs*) ... her laughin' ... punchin' that man.

Julie Shouldn't laugh about that!

Mark The Social Worker.

Julie Mum shoutin' at him down the street, sayin' she knew more than he did!

Mark (*Laughing.*) Dropped his bag. All fell out!

Julie (*Laughing.*) That time you were in the hospital and you made Mum that 'orrible wicker basket.

Mark Don't remember. No. (*With panic.*) No! (*Calmer. Remembering.*) Dad.

Julie Can't remember him very much.

Mark Shoutin', starin' at me.

Julie I was scared of 'im.

Mark Hit Mum wiv 'is fist ... made her cry.

Julie Better off without him eh?

Mark Yeah. Gone!

Julie Out the door.

Mark Good. (*Pause.*) Didn't like me anyway. (*Pause.*)

Julie Mum didn't leave you like Dad did. It's different.

Mark Different!

Julie Mum had to go cos she got ill an' it's better that she died.

Mark (*Into distance.*) Better!

Julie Not that she didn't like you or me.

Mark Yeah ... (*Getting upset.*) ... My friend.

Julie My friend ...

(*To audience.*) There were some things I never told Mum. Like why I was always fightin' at school. They used to say: 'You must be funny too cos you've got a funny brother'. Well that didn't bother me. I knew I was all right. But let them start on Mark, calling him 'SPAZZY, MENTAL, FUNNY IN THE HEAD'. I'd get so wound up, I'd go for 'em – punchin', kickin'. I still get angry when people look at him and laugh or when mums pull their kids away from him as he walks past on the street. I mean, what do they think he's gonna do? Look at 'im! He couldn't harm a fly. (*Pause.*)

Mark (*Crying.*) Miss her.

Julie (*She puts her hand to her head in disbelief.*)What? Err ... that seagull's just shit on my head!

Mark What? Which one? (*Pointing.*) That one?

Julie How the hell do I know?

Mark Come here. (*He moves to her.*) Yurr ... it's all green! Come on. (*He takes her by the hand.*) We'll have to wash it out. (*Mark takes Julie to the sea. He jumps in.*)

Julie Take your shoes off!

Mark What? (*Mark realises he's got his shoes on and jumps out of the water.*)

Julie (*Annoyed.*) Oh Mark!

Mark (*Innocently.*) I'm all wet now! (*Mark removes his shoes and takes hold of Julie's hand.*) Come on! (*They both jump into the water. It is freezing. Mark washes Julie's hair.*) Trust you! (*Julie looks at him. He continues washing her hair.*) There!

Julie Is it all gone?

Mark Yeah.

Julie Are you sure?

Mark (*Angry.*) Yeah! (*Julie steps out of the sea and crosses to the rocks. She suddenly stops and is obviously shocked. Mark jumps out of the water and grabs his shoes*) ... thinks I'm daft. Not that daft!

(*To audience.*) Fore we come away, we went shoppin'. Bought this shirt. I picked it. Julie didn't. The shop man said: 'What colour does he want?' Didn't ask me. 'Green', she said. I picked red. That show'd her! They all do it. Mrs Jenkins, down the street ... when Mum died, she come up to me and Julie. She said: 'I'm sorry to hear about your Mum, Julie. How's he taking it?'

Julie (*Obviously upset by what she sees behind the rock.*) Mark. Look!

Mark What?

Julie Look.

Mark What? What you lookin' at? (*He climbs onto rocks.*)

Julie There.

Mark It's a bird ... (*He picks it up.*) ... It's hurt. Take it to the vet.

Julie Too late.

Mark Why?

Julie It's dead.

Mark Dead. (*Pause.*) ... I'll put it in the sand, eh?

Julie Yeah.

Mark Yeah. (*Mark takes the bird to where the building bricks are. He rearranges blocks. Julie cries soundlessly. Mark concerned, turns to look at her.*) What?

Julie (*Stifling tears.*) It's all right, Mark. Take no notice. I'll be all right. (*She goes to deck-chair.*)

Mark What? (*He notices bird again and goes back to building the sandcastle around it. Julie angrily rushes sand from her feet before putting her shoes on.*)

Julie 'Oh no, Mrs Sutton. He's a lovely baby. Nothin' wrong with him. Look at him.' You knew didn't you Mum – that he wasn't right. But it was something you couldn't put your finger on. You just knew he was different to me – not feedin' right, crying all the time, throwing tantrums, always wanting your attention. But you didn't like to keep botherin' the clinic because they'd think you were fussin'. Another hypochondriac mother wasting the doctor's time. (*To audience.*) They never told her till he was four years old. They said he was hyper-active. Well that explained all the screaming and the running around and that he might be a bit backward but he'd probably be all right if he went to an ordinary school, that he'd catch up. He didn't.

Mark accidentally knocks down part of the sandcastle he is building.

Mark Stupid!

Julie 'Why is he like that? What did I do? It must be my fault.' You did nothing. 'I worked until I was seven months gone.' You needed the money! 'They told me I should drink a pint of milk a day but I couldn't afford it – I had you to look after. Perhaps I had you too close together – there's only eleven months between you.' It's got nothing to do with that! 'I know what it is. It's a punishment!' Look Mum, it could happen to anyone. He's like that cos that's the way he is.

Mark (*Looks up.*) Wot's she lookin' at? What? (*Pause.*) *He resumes building.*

Julie (*Going over to Mark.*) Dad hated him. Yeah, hated him. Cos you weren't gonna be a boxer or a famous footballer, you weren't worth having' in 'is book. Damaged goods! And whose fault was it? ... (*Turning to her imaginary Mum.*) 'You stupid cow. Can't even get that right – can't even give me a proper son.' Course she'd committed the cardinal sin of 'avin' a girl first! (*She moves to rocks, remembering.*) While

Mum was ill, we used to sit and talk – Mark was out at the Training Centre. It was like when I was a kid – after Mark had gone to bed. That was my time with my Mum. I'd pretend I didn't 'ave a brother. (*To Mark.*) Then you'd always come down cos you 'd want a glass of water or a biscuit. As if you didn't get enough attention. I only had TWO HOURS – that was MY time with MY Mum and YOU had to spoil it!

Mark (*Hears this last bit.*) Wot you doin'?

Julie (*Startled.*) Nothing'.

Mark What?

Julie Thinking. (*Pause. Mark resumes building. To Mum.*) I don't know what you're so worried about. You went and saw the place. It's not like a Sub-normality hospital. He'll be sharing a flat with four others. He'll have his own room and he can come and go as he pleases. He'll have responsibility for the cooking, cleaning, paying bills and he'll have a say in how the place is run. He'll learn how to look after himself – become his own person. Kids usually grow up and move away you know. He shouldn't be any different. (*Walking over to Mum.*) And then you can begin to have a life of your own. You haven't had that. Be honest. Oh I know you'll miss him but he's got the right to his own life – he's not just an appendage of you, y'know. (*Pause. Wearily.*) Oh listen to me. The Claire Rayner of Scarborough!

Mark (*Looks at bird.*) Why did it die Julie?

Julie Because it's covered in oil and it couldn't fly away.

Mark Like Mum.

Julie Like me if I'm not careful. (*She goes over to Mark and touches his shoulder lightly.*) What you doin'?

Mark (*Upset.*) What?

Julie It's good.

Mark (*Brightly.*) Yeah!

Julie (*Upset.*) Why did you have to die now?

Mark (*To audience.*) Good innit? D'you go to work? … I do! We start baby bottles next week. Big order from Boots. Mr Johnson says we always get work cos we're cheaper than anyone else.

Julie (*Snaps.*) Cos you're cheap labour.

Mark What? (*To audience.*) Like yer shoes! Where'd you get 'em? … I bet I earn more than you do.

Julie (*Irritated but weary.*) Keep your voice down!

Mark What? (*To audience. Whispers.*) How much? … I get £4 a week. (*He notices something in distance.*) Wot they doin'? Wot? (*He climbs on to rocks.*) They're kissin! (*Pause.*) They're gettin' undressed now.

Julie (*Continues sun-bathing.*) They're probably going for a swim.

Mark (*He stares into distance and slowly tilts his head.*) Don't think they're swimmin' Julie. (*Pause.*) Don't … stop that, they'll scare that dog away. Told you!

Julie (*Sits up.*) What are you lookin' at?

Mark They're having' it off!

Julie (*Astounded.*) You what?!

Mark They are. That's not swimmin'.

Julie runs and joins Mark on the rocks. She tilts her head and peers in same direction as Mark.

Julie (*Smiling.*) They are an' all!

Mark Told you!

Julie (*Pretending to be angry, she pushes Mark off the rock.*) You shouldn't be lookin'.

Mark Well I couldn't help it. They're doin' it in the middle of the beach.

Julie Shh! (*Mark jumps up and down waving at the couple.*)

Mark (*Shouts.*) We know what you're doin'! We know …

Julie (*Yanks him to the ground.*) Mark! (*She grabs a biscuit and stuffs it in Mark's mouth.*) Eat that! (*Julie is *obviously embarrassed. Mark continues to look between Julie and the lovers. Finally:*)

Mark I hope you an' Trev don't do that. Do ya?

Julie (*Outraged.*) You should mind your own business, you cheeky monkey!

Mark You ask me what I do wiv Denise!

Julie That's different.

Mark Why? (*Pause.*)

Julie (*Hesitantly.*) Well you don't do you?

Mark What?

Julie You and Denise. (*Pause.*)

Mark Not allowed. Don't let ya.

Julie Who?

Mark Mum. Denise's Mum and Dad. People. At the Centre. (*Remembering.*) See you 'oldin' 'ands, they shout: 'stop that funny business!'

Julie (*Thinking to herself.*) I've thought of buying him sex.

Mark (*Brightly.*) It'll be fun livin' wiv you and Trevor.

Julie (*Immediately wound up.*) But you're not goin' to live with me and Trevor.

Mark Yes I am.

Julie Where'd you get that idea?

Mark What?

Julie Where'd you get that idea?

Mark (*Innocently.*) I thought it.

Julie You're going tomorrow, remember.

Mark I'm not.

Julie Look, don't you understand? I don't want to be with you all the time. You get in the way.

Mark You get in the way, you do!

Julie You're noisy. It's never quiet with you around. I can't always do the things I want to do.

Mark Mum wouldn't send me away.

Julie More fool her!

Mark She loved me.

Julie (*Snaps.*) Now don't start that. You overstep the mark sometimes you do.

Julie (*Seeing a joke.*) Mark! Boom! Boom! Beat ya!

Julie (*By now very angry.*) I mean it. You're selfish you are. Everything has to revolve round you, dunnit? You just put on your puppy eyes and you get whatever you want. 'Oh feel sorry for me, I'm mentally handicapped.'

Mark (*Turning from her.*) No!!

Julie The world's not like that. People don't wanna know. I'm gonna make you take charge of your own life if it kills me!

Mark (*Trying to get away.*) I'm not goin'!

Julie (*Following him, she grabs him.*) Look. Look at me. I know you're scared. I know that's why you don't want to go. But you've got to stand up for yourself. I'm not always gonna be here. Think of me for a change. There are times when I want to be with Trevor on me own. If a job comes up in say ... Christ I dunno ... Manchester. I wanna be free to take it ... I don't want to be thinking of you all the time. (*Mark desperately moves away, exasperated.*) Look, it's hard enough for me as it is. Because everyone expects me to just give up my life to look after you. Do you know that?

Mark No!!! (*Moves away.*)

Julie (*This is the last straw.*) Oh why weren't you born normal? I wish Mum had stuck that pillow over your face when you were little. (*Pause.*)

Mark (*He turns to Julie and screams.*) I hate you!!! (*He lunges at her and misses. He grabs his shoes, puts them on and attempts to tie his laces – he can't. He becomes more and more frustrated and angry. Julie softens and turns to see what he is doing. She notices his pathetic inability to tie his shoe-laces and goes towards him.*)

Julie Oh come on. Come here!

Mark No. Go away!! No!!

Julie (*Undeterred, she leans over to tie his laces.*) Mark, I just want to ...

Mark (*He gets up wildly and fights Julie back across the stage.*) Noooo!!!! (*Mark is in some sort of fit. His speech is a terrified stream of consciousness. Julie watches helplessly.*) I'm not goin' in that naughty room. Can't get out. Long time. Cold. Dark. No windows, nothin'. Give ya pills. Can't fink. Sleepy. Needles in the arm.

Julie (*She advances towards Mark.*) What are you talking about?

Mark (*He backs off, panic-stricken.*) Don't hit me! Please! Please! Sorry! Get up now. Eat now! Toilet now! Day room now! Nothin' now! Bed now! Mess up routine! Sorry! Sorry! Sorry! (*Mark stands, jerking convulsively. Crying. Fighting off imaginary enemies. Julies goes towards him trying to establish physical contact to calm him.*)

Julie It's all right Mark. I'm here. Julie's here. I didn't know. It's all right. Ssshh! It's all right Mark. It's Julie. Ssshh! (*Julie eventually takes hold of Mark's arms. His whole body is racked with sobs. Cradling him in her arms, they drop to the floor where Mark cries like a baby and Julie rocks him gently.*) Ssshh! Come on. It's all right Mark. Ssshh! Ssshh! (*She hums 'Edelweiss'. This calms Mark considerably. She looks at the audience accusingly. At the end of the song, Julie drags him to his feet.*) Come on. Talk to me about somethin' else. Don't cry. Come on. (*They pace.*) Come on. Talk to me.

Mark What?

Julie Talk about ... that time when you got lost and the police brought you back.

Mark When I got lost?

Julie Remember. You used to get yourself lost once a

week and the police would bring you back and you'd have a bag of sweets.

Mark Oh yeah! Yeah!

Julie And this went on for a long time didn't it?

Mark Yeah.

Julie And what did the police say to Mum in the end?

Mark Don't remember.

Julie Yes you do. That ... you shouldn't be allowed ...

Mark Shouldn't be allowed out on me own.

Julie And Mum said: 'Oh it's funny he can find his own way home four nights of the week'.

Mark Yeah.

Julie And then she turned to you and said: 'Why do you keep botherin' the police?' And what did you say?

Mark Cos they keep givin' me sweets!

Julie (*Smiling.*) And he went all red ...

Mark All red.

Julie That Sergeant. Cos he knew you'd taken the mickey out of 'im.

Mark Taken the mickey. Makes a change. (*Pause.*) Stop now.

Julie (*They stop. Julie looks at Mark and notices his untied laces.*) Oh look at the state of ya! You'll trip up. Sit down.

Mark What?

Julie Sit down. (*They sit. Julie is insistent.*) Now watch! (*She takes one set of laces and demonstrates tying them. Mark watches intently.*) Now you got your two laces right – cross 'em over – now that one has got to go in there like that, right? Now take both ends and pull – like that see – now you're going to make a loop with this one right – so watch, watch – there's your finger right – now make a loop round your finger and hold it at the bottom, right – now this one has got to go all the way round the outside – so, watch, watch – right. Now this is the hard bit – you've got to make another loop by pushing that through there with your finger – right, so you got a loop there and a loop there – now pull gently – there, see – now you have a go.

Mark What?

Julie You heard! (*There follows a long moment between them. Julie is almost daring him to have a go. Mark glances between Julie and his unlaced foot. He decides to have a go. Throughout, it is extraordinarily difficult for him: instruction – assimilation – carrying out of instruction.*) Two laces – cross 'em over – cross 'em – cross 'em – right – now that one goes in there – go on – right. Now take hold of the ends – the other one too – right – now pull – now you've got to make a loop like I showed you – round your finger – right – well hold it at the bottom – right – now that one goes all the way round – gently. Make sure that loop stays up – there – now you've got to push that one through there like that – come on, you do it! Right now you've got the two loops, one there and one there – now pull – pull. There!

Mark (*Triumphantly.*) Yeah!! (*Julie is quietly proud.*)

Julie I bet Denise has missed you this week.

Mark 'Spect she has. I'll buy her a present, eh?

Julie Yeah.

Mark What?

Julie You could get her some perfume. They do little bottles of like Devon Violets, Cologne stuff.

Mark What? Spray?

Julie Yeah or just sort of dab-it-on.

Mark How much?

Julie Dunno. Not much. Coulpa quid I s'pose.

Mark 'Ow mu … two?

Julie Yeah.

Mark I only get four.

Julie I'll help you out.

Mark And a bow.

Julie A bow?

Mark Yeah on it!

Julie Oh yeah. Yeah.

Mark And paper.

Julie Yeah, wrap it up nice – she'll like that.

Mark Yeah. And give that. Right. You get somethin' for Trevor.

Julie Huh. Oh he'll be lucky if he gets a sticka rock!

Mark Buy 'im somethin' for the car!

Julie Bloody car!

Mark Yeah. Buy 'im some .... dice. Furry!

Julie (*Laughing.*) Oh no!

Mark Yeah. They're nice!

Julie You like 'em do ya?

Mark Yeah.

Julie I don't know about that.

Mark Trev likes 'em!

Julie (*Disapproving.*) Mmmm.

Mark He's all right Trev. He's got dirty 'ands though.

Julie (*Laughing.*) What?

Mark Oil and muck. He should scrub 'em!

Julie Have to use Swarfega.

Mark What?

Julie Swarfega. It's this stuff that you put on your hands to take the oil off cos water don't take oil off.

Mark Buy 'im some o' that.

Julie Not a very nice present is it?

Mark Give 'im the hint though! (*They both laugh.*)

Julie Could put a bow on it!

Mark Yeah. And wrap it up. He'd fink it a real present. See his face!

Julie You'd love to get me in trouble. Wouldn't ya?

Mark Yeah ... No!

Julie I don't believe you! (*Pause.*)

Mark Ya do! (*They laugh. Mark looks round. Spies cassette and says coyly:*) Can I play the cassette?

Julie Yeah.

Mark (*Shouts at the top of his voice.*) Yeah!!

Julie Not too loud though! (*Mark plays around with the cassette player while Julie starts to pack away the picnic things.* Abba's 'Under attack' *is on first.*)

Mark Abba!! (*Mark fast-forwards the tape on to* 'Oh Julie' *by* Shakin' Stevens *at which he becomes very excited.*) Shakin' Stevens!!! Julie!!! (*He begins to mime along to the record doing* Shakin' Stevens *impressions. Julie is very embarrassed. She continues to pack away the picnic things. By the end of the song she is in the deck-chair with her sunglasses on, hiding behind her paperback novel. The song ends.*) What? Bow! (*Moving to Julie.*) Why you hidin'? What? ('Knowing me, knowing you' *by* Abba *starts up on the tape. Mark gets very excited.*) What? It's Abba!!! Dance, Julie!!

Julie (*Outraged.*) Do what?

Mark I'll teach ya to waltz.

Julie No!

Mark Come on!

Julie (*She pans round the audience and smiles. Takes off sunglasses.*) All right. (*She gets up from deck-chair.*) Now I don't know how to do this. You'll have to show me. (*They face one another.*)

Mark Right. (*Mark grabs Julie's left hand and puts it on his shoulder.*) Put that there. (*He yanks the other arm and stretches it out in tango style.*) An' put that there.

Julie (*Smiling.*) Right.

Mark That foot. (*Treads on her toe.*)

Julie Oww!

Mark Sorry! That foot goes that way!

Julie Right.

Mark And that foot goes that way.

Julie (*Laughing because he has directed her in an outlandish direction.*) Right.

Mark Then you bring 'em together. And you count in threes.

Julie And ... 1 ... 2 3

Mark/Julie 1 ... 2 ... 3 ... 1 ... 2 ... 3 ... 1 ... 2 ... 3 (*They begin to waltz getting faster and more confident until:*)

Mark You're leadin'!!

Julie Sorry!

Mark Again! And 1 ... 2 ... 3

Mark/Julie 1 ... 2 ... 3 ... 1 ... 2 ... 3 ... 1 ... 2 ... 3 (*They both laugh and begin to enjoy themselves. Julie then notices something off-stage. She breaks away from Mark.*)

Julie (*To off-stage.*) What? What did you say? Come 'ere and say that! ...

Mark (*Softly.*) No.

Julie (*Very angry.*) Come 'ere and say that! (*Mark becomes agitated. He tries to placate Julie. He keeps up a continuous stream of:*)

Mark Don't matta Julie. Please Julie. Don't! It don't matta!

Julie ... Oh 'ark at him! Have YOU looked in the mirror lately mate? Oh naff off! YOU shouldn't be allowed on it. People like you make me SICK! Oh yeah? Up yours an' all. Up yours!

Mark Don't matta Julie. IT DON'T MATTA!

Julie (*Rounding on Mark.*) It does matter. Don't let people call you names like that – I can't bear it! Just turn round and say: 'You're the ones that are mad'. Because they are. It's not you!

Mark (*Upset.*) Well?

Julie (*Exasperated.*) You've got to stand up for yourself. Those berks earlier on. You just took it, didn't ya?

Mark (*Evasion tactics again.*) It's hard ...

Julie I know it's hard but you've got to do it. I can't do it for ya! Fight back! (*Mark turns his back on her.*) You Jerk! You spazz! (*Mark puts his hands to his ears and screams.*)

Mark No! No! No!

Julie You stupid mong! (*She realises what she has said and breaks down. Mark cries.* 'Knowing me, Knowing you' *continues. Julie regains control. She turns off cassette player.*) D' ya fancy an ice-cream?

Mark (*Covering up.*) Yeah!

Julie If I give ya the money d' ya wanna go and get 'em? (*Mark nods. Julie goes to handbag.*) Come here then. Now here's a pound. You won't want more than that. You want two cornets an' twenty pence change.

Mark Not trumpets!

Julie (*This is obviously an old joke.*) Cornets!! And twenty pence change.

Mark Twenty pence change.

Julie Off you go then. (*Exit Mark. Julie watches him go. She sits in the deck-chair peering after him worriedly. Mark re-enters with cornets. Julie picks up her paperback and pretends to read it intently.*)

Mark (*Proferring ice-cream.*) 'eeyar!

Julie (*Feigning surprise.*) Oh ta!

Mark An' twenty pence change.

Julie Oh keep it!

Mark Ta! (*Mark sits beside Julie on the sand. They both stare at their ice-creams and smile, looking at one another. They laugh. They pan round the audience.*

Then they both plunge their ice-creams to their foreheads and fall about laughing. They clean themselves up and begin to eat their ice-creams.) Good!

Julie Ja have to go far?

Mark No. (*They eat their ice-creams. It starts to rain. Julie notices.*)

Julie Here y'are. Hold that. (*Julie hands Mark her ice-cream. She puts up the umbrella.*) Give us me ice-cream back! Ta! (*She goes and sits under the umbrella. She watches Mark get rained on. He slowly realises it is raining.*)

Mark Julie, it's rain …

Julie (*Laughing.*) Come here!

Mark What? (*Notices where Julie is and quickly clambers towards her.*) Ya mighta told me! (*Pause.*) This the best 'oliday I've ever 'ad! It's FUN!!

Julie (*Thinking.*) What time is it?

Mark What? (*Looks at watch.*) Twenny ta five!

Julie Your teacher at school said you'd never learn to tell the time.

Mark What? … Mum taught me. Two weeks.

Julie (*Turning to him.*) See you can do things when you want to! (*Pause.*)

Mark I don't know wot to do Julie.

Julie (*Sighing.*) I'm not gonna make you go – it's up to you. (*Pause. The rain stops. Julie notices and stands up. She goes to her bags.*) Eeyar Mark. It's stopped!

Mark What!

Julie (*Picking up stuff.*) Tell you what … I'll race ya!! (*She starts to run.*)

Mark Wot?

Julie I'm winnin'!!

Mark Wot? (*Mark scrambles out from under the umbrella excitedly laughing and screaming. He collects his* *belongings together.*) That's not fair! Wait for me! Julie! (*Laughs.*) You 'ad a head start! Wait for me! (*Taped voices off:*)

Voice 1 Oh look who it is!

Voice 2 Mong, Wally.

Voice 3 Spazz Features.

Voice 1 Bet your Mum had a fit when she saw you! (*Laughter.*) Plastic Spastic.

(*Voice 1 begins a chant.*) Plastic Spastic/Plastic Spastic/Plastic Spastic.

Voices 2 and 3 join in. The chant becomes faster and faster. Mark becomes increasingly agitated as the chant continues. He drops his belongings but keeps hold of his football. He keeps looking at where the voices are coming from. He gradually picks up courage and is about to fight back. The chant becomes louder and reaches a crescendo. Mark finally opens his mouth but cannot speak. He crumbles and cries in anguish. He throws the ball away. It hits the sandcastle and it collapses. He runs off shouting:

Mark No! No! No! (*The sound of* 'Under attack' *by* Abba *is gradually heard.*)

Curtain

'HOT-SEATING' GUIDELINES

Second Tour: May – June 1984

Compiled by: Lawrence Evans
Gill Nathanson

The following outline of how we ran our 'hot-seating' session is obviously intended merely as a guide.

During the break, following the play, we reorganised the chairs into two semi-circles. After the audience had congregated, they were asked to divide themselves evenly between the two sets of chairs. They were also given the following information:

1 It is one week since Julie and Mark returned from their holiday.

2 Mark is supposed to be going to Northfields (a place you've heard about in the play) tomorrow.

3 You will have a chance to talk to both Mark and Julie and ask them any questions that you might have.

Enter Mark and Julie.

Julie Mark!

Mark What?

Julie Well ... have you made yer mind up? Are you going?

Mark Going where?

Julie You know where!

Mark I've not decided yet.

Julie What d'ya mean? You were packed and ready to go yesterday.

Mark I changed me mind.

Julie I don't believe it!

Mark Well believe it! I can if I want. It's up to me!

Julie What about me? ...

They part (still muttering) to go to separate groups. They spend approximately 15 minutes' 'hot-seating' before swapping over groups. (In our production, Julie facilitated this.)

The 'hot-seating' served the dual purpose of encouraging the audience to question, on a deeper level, their and society's attitudes to mental handicap through addressing themselves to the characters' concrete problem of whether Mark should go to Northfields. Both actors had specific lines to follow which we felt facilitated this process.

For example:

Julie I can't understand why Mark doesn't want to go to Northfields.

This usually started off an argument about the need for security versus the need for independence.

Julie Why should I be responsible for Mark? Mark has a right to his own life away from me. I have a right to my own life too.

Again, this leads on to arguments about the family versus the State's responsibility to give people like Mark the help they need to achieve an independent life.

Another important aspect of Julie's 'hot-seating' would be to challenge the notion of women in the family being the most suitable people to take the role of carers of mentally handicapped people.

Julie If I was Mark's brother, would people expect me to look after him?

No!

So what difference does it make that I'm his sister?

Mark's 'hot-seating' challenged in a slightly different way. The actor's line was to look at the concept of prejudice.

Mark Have you got sisters?

Do they talk at you all the time?

What d' ya do about it?

This lead to a discussion on 'fighting back' and raised questions such as the use of violence, both verbal and physical and ways of dealing with it.

Mark Do people call ya names?

What?

Why do they call ya names?

People call me names. Why?

Again this lead the discussion on to name calling and why people do it and eventually on to the area of 'difference'. The difference between Mark and other people. Why people are afraid of people like Mark, and how and why that misconception is perpetuated.

This lead the group to discuss the concept of power within our society. Who has power? How is it used?

Mark Do people talk down to ya?

They do it to me too!

Why do people talk down to ya?

At the end of the thirty minutes, the characters and audience come together for a final few minutes in order to answer, jointly now, any final questions in character.

We then talked to the group *out of character*. In this last part of the session, we could try to highlight any issues raised by the audience during the 'hot-seating'. For example:

1 The position of women as carers in our society.
2 The need to label sections of our society (what the label 'mentally handicapped' means). Are labels positive/negative?
3 Because mentally handicapped people are generally 'non-producers' in our society, they seem to be treated as being worthless.

QUESTIONS AND EXPLORATIONS

The Best Years of Your Life

1 Keeping Track

Scenes One and Two

1. What are your first impressions of Robert's father?
2. Summarise what you have learned about Robert's situation in these first two scenes.

Scenes Three and Four

3. Describe the relationship between Robert and Mark. What sort of person is Mark?
4. Why has Dave come to see Robert? Do you think the gifts were suitable?
5. How much do the people at the club know about Robert's illness?

Scenes Five and Six

6. What do we learn in these two scenes about the physical problems Robert now has to face?
7. Why do you think Robert will not open the door for Mrs Hurst?
8. Write the conversation Mrs Hurst and Robert's father had when she telephoned to tell him about the incident.
9. Describe how the different people in the pub respond to Robert.
10. The stage directions tell us that Robert is 'under

unbearable pressure'. Why do you think he feels this way? Why does he behave so strangely to Paula and Linda?

Scenes Seven and Eight

11 Robert explains some of his feelings in Scene Seven. Write his diary entry for that evening until Mark tells him to 'shut up'. Include his feelings as well as an account of events.

12 Why does Mark get angry with Robert at the end of the scene?

13 What more do we learn about Robert's father in Scene Eight? What are your feelings towards him? What do we learn about the family history?

Scenes Nine and Ten

14 Using information from both scenes, discuss the sort of pressure Mark has been under for the last year.

15 Why does Robert change his mind about going to the football match?

16 Why doesn't Robert tell the others the truth about his illness? Do you agree with him or Mark? Give reasons for your answer.

17 How is Mark feeling about Robert's lies?

Scenes Eleven and Twelve

18 What do we learn about Robert, and how important football is to him, in Scene Eleven?

19 In Scene Twelve we learn more details about some of the side effects of Robert's illness. Why do you think the author goes into such detail? Discuss how Mark might be feeling outside the cubicle.

Scenes Thirteen and Fourteen

20 What do you think Robert means when he says 'you never stop to think how great things are'? Do you agree?

21 What new things do we learn about the family background? Discuss how close Mark and Robert have become during the play.

22 Why is Mark trying to make his father angry in Scene Fourteen?

Scenes Fifteen and Sixteen

23 Write a few sentences about the father. How does he cope with emotional stress?

24 Who is Gary and why is he at the football ground? What is the significance of his brief appearance in the play?

2 Explorations

A Characters

1. Robert is only seventeen and with a promising future as a footballer ahead of him. What difference does this make to your reactions when reading the play?
2. In the form of a diary trace in detail how Mark reacts to, and comes to terms with, Robert's illness.
3. How are the hospital and their staff presented in the play?
4. Read Scenes Fourteen and Fifteen again. 'Hot-seat' Robert's father in role. Try to discover how he felt after Mark had become angry with him. How does he feel he has behaved? Has he been a 'good' father? What

memories has Robert's illness revived? What is he going to do now?

5 Write a character study of the father. Consider his reaction to Robert's illness and how he faced emotional crises. Think about how he coped with his wife's death and how he eventually faces up to Robert's illness.

6 Why do you think the author has made the family consist of three men? Were you surprised by any of their behaviour? In what ways is their behaviour typical? How does their behaviour differ from what you might expect?

B Themes

1 Explain the significance of the title of the play.

2 Robert feels self-conscious in his wheelchair. He thinks that people see only his illness and not him as a person. In a group discuss whether his fears appear to be founded **a** when he visits the pub, and **b** when he goes to the football club.

Do you think that there is prejudice against wheelchair users? Why does this exist? What does and what can society do to change this?

3 Robert faces quite a few physical problems as a wheelchair user. In groups discuss how such a user might cope with **a** public transport, **b** shopping in your local high street, **c** being a pupil in your school.

4 The majority of physically disabled children in this country receive segregated education which often means they do not achieve their full potential.[1]

1 *Disabled People in Britain and Discrimination*, Colin Barnes (Hurst and Co., London 1991)

In the UK only 0.3 per cent of higher education students are disabled although disabled people are 10 per cent of the population.[2]

Discuss these two statements. Try to write down some reasons why disabled pupils are treated differently from the able-bodied. Do you think there is anything that could be done to improve the situation? What would you do to make opportunities more equal?

5 Disabled people in the UK are three times more likely to be unemployed than any other group.[3]

Disabled men in full-time work in the UK earn almost a quarter less than non-disabled men, and disabled women earn a third less than disabled men.

Discuss these two statements and try to decide why they should be true. Why might employers be reluctant to employ a disabled person, and when they are employed why are wages often lower? There are equal opportunities laws to encourage employment of disabled men and women but these are seldom enforced – why? Do you think that society should do more to include people with disabilities?

Lives Worth Living

1 Keeping Track

1 What do you think is the significance of the music that is playing in the opening scene?

2 and 3 *Disabled People in Britain and Discrimination*, Colin Barnes (Hurst and Co., London 1991)

2 Why do you think the voices are off-stage and the people not seen to the audience?

3 Why is Julie 'annoyed' with Mark?

4 What purpose is served by Mark talking to the audience on pages 65 to 66. How do you think they would react?

5 Julie ignores Mark's conversation until he starts talking about girlfriends and boyfriends. Why do you think she only reacts then?

6 On pages 67 and 68 Mark and Julie are talking about the same thing, Mark working at Northfields, but they are not actually listening to each other. Write a paragraph each on Mark and Julie explaining their different outlooks and feelings.

7 Why does Mark shout out about the seagull?

8 'He doesn't miss a trick' (page 67) seems a strange thing to say about Mark. What prompts this comment? Think about what you have read so far and write a couple of paragraphs about Mark. Write about the things he is able to do as well as the things he finds difficult to understand.

9 Mark tells the audience that he has a job, unlike Julie. What kind of job does he have?

10 Explain Julie's work situation.

11 On pages 73 to 78 we learn a lot about Mark's and Julie's childhood. Write a couple of paragraphs about their experiences and their family relationships.

12 Explain the significance of Julie comparing herself to a dead bird on page 78.

13 On page 80 Julie is 'outraged'. Why? Give reasons for your answers.

14 Mark points out that Julie asks him about him and Denise. Is it 'different'? Should it be 'different'?

15 Where is Mark meant to be going after the holiday is over?

16 What clues does Mark's panic and stream of consciousness on page 82 give us about life in an institution?

17 What does the incident on pages 82 to 83 tell us about Mark's personality? What does it tell us about how some people respond to disability?

18 Why do you think Julie smiles at the audience before agreeing to dance with Mark?

19 Julie's outburst and name calling on page 87 to 88 are a measure of how frustrated and angry she gets with both Mark and the bullies. What do you think would be the best response from Mark when such incidents occur? Give reasons for your answer.

20 Discuss with a partner why you think the play ended in almost the same way as it started. What has changed?

2 Explorations

A In Performance

1 A soliloquy is a speech in a play delivered by one person and aimed at the audience. Find examples of this by both Mark and Julie in the play.

Write or improvise a soliloquy for Mark, outlining his mixed feelings about going to Northfields. For example, he has met friends and is usefully occupied but his wages are an insulting £4.00 a week. It should include something on how he is treated.

2 The audience are directly addressed on several occasions by both Mark and Julie. Why is this technique used? Who do the audience represent? How do you think they might respond to Mark at first? Does their attitude change as the play progresses? If so, why?

B Character

1 Think about the character of Julie. Write down six words or phrases that might describe her personality, eg. strong-willed. Then choose incidents from the play that support your statements.

Now look at how she feels about Mark. She often has mixed feelings about him, eg. as a child she defended him and yet resented all the time he took up with their mother. How is this ambivalence shown now she is an adult? Remember that the stage directions can give important clues to people's feelings.

When you have gathered enough information write a character study of Julie, or hot-seat someone in role, by asking them questions and then having them reply in character.

C An Extra Scene

1 Julie has returned from holiday and is talking to Trevor about Mark and the future that all three of them might share in some way. Trevor likes Mark and is obviously understanding but ...

Write or improvise the conversation, in playscript form, that they might have.

D Themes

1 What is the significance of the title 'Lives Worth Living' to both Julie and Mark?

2 For discussion.

Think about how people usually respond to someone who is intellectually impaired. Do attitudes change as you get older? Why do people react in these ways? Are the reactions of the people in the play typical or unusual? What would you have done if you were Julie?

3 These are two statements that Julie might have made about her relationship with Mark. In a group discuss what you think she is saying and decide how far you agree with her. If the responsibility for Mark does not belong with Julie where does it belong?

Julie Why should I be responsible for Mark? Mark has a right to his own life away from me. I have a right to my own life too.

If I was Mark's brother, would people expect me to look after him?
No!
So what difference does it make that I'm his sister?

Then think about who should care for the disabled in society. What help do you think carers should get? What do you think might be an ideal situation? Remember that an element of choice is important for all people.

4 Read the article 'The rewards in making a home for Winnifred' on the following pages and answer the following questions.

a Explain the significant changes in the household since Winnifred's arrival.

b How do people react when they first meet Winnifred?

c What does Winnifred contribute towards family life?

d Select some information from the article which suggests that looking after Winnifred is not straightforward.

The rewards in making a home for Winnifred

Steven Main on how family life has been enriched by the arrival of his mentally handicapped sister-in-law.

Winnifred came into our home, with scant warning, early in March this year. An hour after the brief phone call announcing her imminent arrival she was in permanent residence, ensconced in my favourite armchair and indicating, politely but firmly, that the television was not switched to the channel of *her* choice.

Inheriting a 57-year-old mentally handicapped relative is bound to have a significant impact on one's life, but Winnifred has always lived in the family, first with her mother and, for the past 20 years, with her sister Sheila. Because of illness, Sheila can no longer care for her so she will be living with her other sister – my wife – and myself.

Caring for mentally handicapped people in the community frequently provokes heated debates, usually centring on cost effectiveness, benefit to the mentally handicapped themselves and the effect on people around them. Yet mentally handicapped people such as my sister-in-law have been cared for in the community, often by their families, since man became civilised.

For us the transition has worked well. Several months later, Winnifred is firmly established as part of our family, which now appears to revolve around her: her school, her social life (which is very active) and, above all, her cleaning.

Winnifred loves to clean. She starts the day off fairlylightly with a quick pot-drying and bin-emptying session after breakfast and before the taxi arrives to take her to the centre where she spends her weekdays.

When she arrives home at 4 p.m. there has to be at least an hour's dusting, tidying or polishing before her television programmes start. Woe betide my wife if the house is tidy when she returns home. 'No cups in here, or in here,' grumbles Winnifred as she darts from room to room. 'I'll tidy the shoes shall I?'

Several significant changes have taken place in our household since Winnifred's arrival, quite apart from the constant need to find suitable jobs for her to tackle. First, after a break of many years, we now need a babysitter, for she cannot be left alone. My wife has had to curtail her part-time job because someone has to be at home when Winnifred returns from the centre, and she has to correct the results of Winnifred's enthusiastic, but often ineffectual, housework. She has to bath her, wash her hair, help her to get ready for her day centre and perform all the other duties of a mother with a five-year-old child.

I have become an interested observer of the reaction of friends and acquaintances when they first meet Winnifred and other handicapped people.

Young males act very naturally towards Winnifred. They are usually friendly and helpful; without exception they make eye contact and talk to her in a relaxed, easy-going manner. Young females, middle-aged men and women from more affluent backgrounds, with one or two notable exceptions, find great difficulty in relating to her. They avoid eye contact and make inane remarks on subjects which are of little interest to her.

The warmest reaction comes from women who have led less cosseted existences. A dear friend, who had a very tough time at the end of the war, recently met Winnifred for the first time. Her reaction was immediate and spontaneous; she clutched Winnifred to her bosom, kissed her, fussed her and clucked over her like a mother hen.

Winnifred has difficulty coping with the everyday tensions of family life and resists any attempt to change established behaviour patterns. No matter how gently we try, such attempts always result in outbursts of crying and shouting.

These tantrums were frequent at first, with many threats from her that she was 'going home', but have become fewer as we have all learnt to live together. Winnifred operates within a protected environment, both at home and at the day centre, where she works in the greenhouse or plays dominoes. Even her social life, provided by the Gateway Club, takes place in an atmosphere of loving care and protection.

Only now have I realised from whom she needs protecting – us. Our civilised, materialistic society is extremely hostile to people who cannot read or write, cannot understand television and video sets, money and pedestrian crossings. As a result of these so-called shortcomings, Winnifred and her friends are not highly regarded by our society, which likes to keep them out of sight and out of mind.

FURTHER READING

Poetry

Mentally Handicapped, Danny Cerguena
Hospital, Brian Geary
Visiting Hour, Norman McCaig
Remember Me, Christina Rossetti
Death of a Son, Jon Silkin
Brain Damaged, Margot Stewart

Books

The Bus People, Rachel Anderson (OXFORD 1989)
Welcome Home, Jellybean, Marlene Fauter Shyer (COLLINS CASCADE 1984)
Hunter in the Dark, Monica Hughes (COLLINS CASCADE 1987)
Red Sky in the Morning, Elizabeth Laird (HEINEMANN 1988)
Mama's Going to Buy You a Mockingbird, Jean Little (PENGUIN 1986)
I Can Jump Puddles, Alan Marshall (LONGMAN 1980)
An Open Mind, Susan Sallis (PENGUIN 1988)
Sweet Frannie, Susan Sallis (HEINEMANN 1981)
Dead Bird's Singing, Marc Talbert (LITTLE, BROWN AND COMPANY 1988)
PS Write Soon, Colby Rodowsky (FARRAR, STRAUS AND GIROUX 1988)
Izzy Willy Nilly, Cynthia Voight (COLLINS 1987)

HEINEMANN PLAYS

OTHER TITLES IN THIS SERIES

Children's Ward

Age 12+

Paul Abbott, John Chambers and Kay Mellor
Granada TV

Six scripts from the popular Granada TV series Children's Ward. The plays trace the fortunes of patients admitted to the children's ward and the relationships between them.

Children's Ward also examines the way the programmes are made, and is an excellent medium for discussing the nature of television drama.

ISBN: 435 23285 1

Whose Life is it Anyway? **Age 14+**

Brian Clark

Whose Life is it Anyway? is both a powerful stage-play and major feature film about the struggle of the central character for the right to die.

Completely and permanently paralysed by an accident and dependent on a life-support machine, Ken Harrison challenges the traditional duty of the medical profession to keep him alive at all costs.

ISBN: 435 23287 8